ISBN 978-1-7322915-0-8

In Two Worlds

A Novel

Ido Kedar

To those who have yet to find their voices.

Acknowledgments

This book was an enormous undertaking for me. I learned so much about how to write like a novelist from Leora Romney. Great thanks to her for her insights and editing guidance. Much appreciation also goes to Andrea Widburg for her helpful feedback, Sara Bildner for her sharp eyes and Rich Garbarino for making it look just right. Huge gratitude to Roz Romney for her cover artistry. Finally, I must thank my wonderful parents who have been so supportive throughout my ups and downs, and to my lovely sister, who has joined me on this journey.

Author's Note

I started writing my first book when I was in middle school and finished it when I was in early high school. I felt consumed with a sense of urgency to educate others about the true experiences of a person who has so-called "low-functioning" autism. I have resented my entire life the concept of low and high-functioning when applied to autism. The terms fool people into thinking that all autisms are the same, just differing by the degree of functionality. Nonspeaking people like me, who had no means to communicate and didn't benefit much from years of speech therapy or intensive ABA therapy, were written off in the low-functioning category. Because I alone knew how much I knew—that I could read, spell, calculate, think, and problem solve but remained trapped inside a non-obeying body—I came to have genuine contempt for many of the most arrogant and foolish professionals I saw. This made me cynical at a young age. I think it is much like an innocent person being accused of a deed they didn't do but having no means to counter the incorrect "facts." My autism was explained incorrectly in front of me a thousand times. So, once I became a proficient communicator, I had an urgent need to educate others about the true nature of my misunderstood disability.

My book, *Ido in Autismland: Climbing Out of Autism's Silent Prison*, has surpassed my hopes in changing the conversation about autism. I have seen movement in attitudes and acceptance, but there is still much more that can be improved. In *Ido in Autismland*, I tried to explain what my life was like and counter the widespread belief that nonspeaking autism, long deemed an intellectual, language processing disability, is, for me and for many others, a severe breakdown in the body's ability to respond correctly to the mind's instructions. Though there are people who do have difficulty processing speech and understanding emotions and who struggle with theory of mind or empathetic insight, I myself cannot identify with their challenges because I have a different disability. I have always processed auditory speech at a high level and understood human emotions, but I don't behave normally, not because I don't understand, but because my motor system is so mucked up. Imagine being paralyzed in effect, yet moving around to the body's own commands. This might include impulsive, unpredictable actions, self-stimulatory behavior, challenges with emotional regulation, poor initiation, clumsy movements and the inability to communicate verbally or by handwriting. Over time, well-practiced neural routes get more efficient, allowing more body control in that action. Now I have much more motor control in hundreds of actions that were out of reach for me as a young boy, but I am still far from normal in my motor capacity.

It may be confusing to those observing us because we can do some things well, some things inconsistently, and some things not at all. This confounds scientists, our own parents, and even ourselves. Whatever is going on neurologically to create these challenges remains a mystery. Why should I be able to type on an iPad but not to perform other, seemingly trivial tasks? Who knows? I wish I did. However, it is important that you understand that it took me years to reach the fluency I now enjoy in typing. My index finger touching letters has become a more practiced neurological pathway for me. Because of this inconsistency in performance, nonspeaking autism remains a source of confusion to researchers and specialists. Yet the inconsistency itself sheds light on something, I imagine, that could help us to understand this neurological condition better.

I have been blogging for many years about autism. My blog and my book have been used as a source of information for people to learn about autism from a person with autism. That may sound kind of obvious, but it is far from commonplace. Historically, autism has been described by non-autistic experts who look at our outsides and claim to understand our insides. Because many of the objects of their expertise had no means to communicate or correct their ideas, little changed in theories or treatment. However, over the last decade or so, more and more autistic people have been learning to communicate by pointing to letters on boards or by typing on augmentative communication devices. To be precise, that means typing using one finger. Our motor systems remain inconsistent, as I mentioned, and ten-finger typing demands a degree of fine motor control beyond the ability of one with severe body apraxia.

I became interested in writing another book when someone suggested to me that I should consider writing a novel. I loved the idea of writing fiction because it gave me the chance to be creative, to delve deeply into a character and his story, and to be able to describe more aspects of autism from many angles. I believe this book is the first novel ever written by a person with nonspeaking autism who touches letters to communicate. It is my own work. No one else wrote it. I wish I didn't need to say that but I believe I still do.

I suspect many people will assume that Anthony is me and I am Anthony, but he is not me and I am not him. This is a work of fiction. I certainly used my own experiences to help me understand him, and some of his experiences did happen to me, but many of them did not and are the products of my imagination. I learned to communicate at the age of seven and Anthony was an older teenager when he finally was taught how to communicate. My family is not his. The other characters are invented, or perhaps inspired by composites of people, but I have met none of them in my own life. Nevertheless, the characters represent real people, and the struggles are the real struggles of parents, siblings and people with autism. It has its heroes and its villains.

In Two Worlds is the story of one boy with autism, yet I think you will find many other people who share some of his story.

1

Beach Day

Anthony enjoyed going to the ocean. He loved the cold water on his hot body. He loved the hot sand tickling his bare feet. He loved the sensory pleasures of the ocean breeze on his skin, the whitecaps breaking and the seabirds running after the waves. He enjoyed finding seaweed that washed ashore and stomping on the air bubbles. Seaweed was enticing. It twirled and trailed after Anthony in fascinating patterns. Putting it all together, the ocean was a huge rush, thrilling every sense, even taste.

"Anthony, take the seaweed out of your mouth!" his mother yelled. The three boys were playing in the sand. Mark had prepared a long path meant to funnel the tide. Little Gary played with his toys, attempting to build a tower of sand. And Anthony, who had resisted all attempts to get him to make his own tunnel or tower, was sitting nearby running sand through his fingers and loving the feel. He stared, mesmerized at the sight of the sand tumbling in falling columns to the sand on his feet. He had to taste it. The urge was overwhelming. Oh no, not again. Anthony's father jumped up.

"No, no!" He brought a towel and wiped Anthony's tongue. The people lying closest to Anthony's family were staring. "Give him some water," his dad yelled to Anthony's mother. "I can't get it all." Then he stared sternly at his son. "No eat sand, Anthony," he said in clipped broken English. "No, bad. Bad."

Part of Anthony wanted to eat more sand just because he hated baby talk so much. Compulsions were hard to take. They were like a body ordering a mind. It wasn't as if Anthony enjoyed a mouth full of sand. It was gritty and tasted salty and he felt a bit like gagging. He saw his brothers pretending they weren't with him. He saw his father's shame. If Anthony could have explained, he would have told his parents that he had to obey the compulsion. It didn't matter that the sand was gross in his mouth or that he looked like a strange oddball to the strangers who were staring with such curiosity. His body ordered him to eat sand, so he ate sand.

His impulsive acts were like a lizard hanging out on a rock and without thought ambushing the cricket that wandered by. Like the lizard, Anthony lived with impulsive actions governed by his primitive brain, but unlike the lizard, they often were not functional. A lizard eats his cricket to survive. Anthony's impulses, like pulling petals off flowers or eating strangers' leftover scraps he found on the tables in the mall food court or putting sand or seaweed in his mouth, seemed idiotic, harmful, or just plain weird. But he had no means to resist these compulsions.

"It isn't good, Anthony," his father said. He took Anthony by the hand to play in the waves. Gary took his father's other hand. The moist sand vanished under Anthony's feet. Anthony bounced up and down on his toes and waved his arms in the air, excited. The three of them jumped over the approaching waves over and over. Finally, Anthony tumbled forward and brought his hand deep into the soft, muddy sand. There was no stopping himself. He put a handful of it into his mouth. "I can't take this any longer," Anthony's father muttered. He brought Anthony and Gary back to the towel. "He did it again," he told Anthony's mother.

"I saw," she said. "Maybe we should go home."

"No, no, no!" cried Gary. "It's not fair!" He was right. The family obeyed Anthony and his impulses too often. "I want to stay longer, please."

"He has autism," Anthony's father yelled to the staring strangers. They turned their heads, embarrassed at being noticed. "Fine, let's go play ball," he called to Gary and Mark, "and maybe," he suggested to Anthony and his mom, "you two can stay here on the towel." Anthony's mom gave him a snack. She poured sand on his legs and dug holes in the sand with him. He started to calm down inside. His mom sang to him and he snuggled next to her. Then she took Anthony by the hand and they went for a stroll by the shore. He felt the velvety sand under his feet squish between his toes with every step. He felt salty and damp. He was happy. When they came back to the towel, after a long walk, Gary's tower stood, pail-shaped, made by inverting damp sand into a multi-tiered edifice.

Anthony had to obey. He stepped on it.

2

Autismland

Anthony lived in two worlds. There was the world inside his head, which was like a wild pleasure palace of colors and lights. It was intoxicating to go there. Anthony retreated into this world for many reasons. He went there for peace, and to escape from unwanted demands. He went there to pass time in a sensory high of movement, color and shimmering light that would make painful feelings drift away for a while. Like an alcoholic getting solace from a bottle, Anthony took solace in his inner world. This was Autismland, a curious land of the mind that was accessible only to a limited number of unintentional occupants. His other world was the outer daily prosaic reality where everyone else lived, too. Anthony was among those chosen by fate to straddle both.

His clumsy hands, mouth and uncooperative body made participation in normal activities hard, so hard he returned often to Autismland for relief, because the outer world was filled with impossible demands. To be in that world, to attempt to blend in with the normals, Anthony had to fight his autistic mind nonstop. Of course, he could *never* fully blend in. But he could *try* to do what people asked him to do as much as possible and try to appear more normal. Anthony wasn't often successful. His dual existence confounded everyone because even when he withdrew into Autismland, his outer shell remained—a detached, remote, enigmatic and sometimes annoying presence. There yet not there. Present but also absent. Who knew that beyond this autistic mask was a clever and creative boy? The answer, sadly, is that no one but Anthony knew.

"Get up, sleepyhead," Anthony's mother called. "Time to get ready for school." Anthony moved slowly, dread filling him suddenly. The thought of another mind-numbing day at school made him want to fall back asleep, but his mother insisted. He flapped his hands in frustration, emitting long vocalizations of meaningless sounds. He badly longed to retreat to Autismland, where lovely, soothing, smooth and intoxicating patterns took him away from the dread and the doubts. "Put-on-shirt," his mom instructed, speaking in the high-pitched, abbreviated, false cheer tones of ABA-speak. Her words pulled him abruptly into his other, frustrating world. "Good job," she cheered on script. "Now put-on-pants."

Baby talk. Anthony rolled his eyes in his mind. His mom had been taught to simplify, over-enunciate and speak to him in attention grabbing pitches by his ABA team. Bright tones. No extras. Don't confuse him with grammar or prepositions.

ABA was short for Applied Behavioral Analysis. It was the educational program Anthony had grown up with since before he turned three. From that time until he started school he'd received forty hours a week of ABA's mental drills. These lessons had been scientifically designed to take a pliable baby brain with autism and build it step by step into a brain that acted like one that didn't have autism. The specialists recommended it strongly, especially in the early years when a child's brain was more plastic, or changeable, and thus created a time-limited "window of opportunity" for progression.

After he started school, Anthony continued to receive this essential treatment in the afternoons and on weekends, though for fewer hours. It was important to maximize his therapies before that window of opportunity closed, and each year it closed a little more.

The real world never really let Anthony alone. Besides the

drills and baby talk, his autistic stims, especially his hand flapping, had to be stopped at all times. It was crucial that he be engaged in activity every moment to minimize his autistic actions. "How will he ever act appropriately if you allow him to engage in these behaviors?" they pressed his parents, who always followed their advice.

The result was that Anthony, all day, each time his hands needed to flap, was told, "No hands," or "Hands down," or the most exasperating phrase of all, "Hands quiet." The fact that Anthony *needed* to flap, that it was hard-wired into his neural networks like blinking, made no difference because flapping hands looked strange. It was socially stigmatizing. It had to be stopped. Revenge fantasies filled his soul. He laughed inside, imagining himself telling his ABA supervisor, Natasha, *Hands quiet!* each time she scratched an itch. The imperative to keep Anthony occupied exhausted his parents.

Throughout his life, an array of autism experts had identified Anthony's many problems with certainty. They knew a great deal about what was wrong with him. They knew he couldn't process language properly and that the reason he couldn't communicate or act on instructions consistently was because he didn't understand words. There were some words he had painstakingly acquired in labeling drills using flashcard pictures, however, and each mastered word and the date of mastery were documented in a data logbook. Anthony's real world was full of treatments that generated volumes of data about him.

The specialists claimed that many autistic kids drilled in the ABA lessons he was receiving were now indistinguishable from typical peers. That's what the developmental pediatrician had told his parents when he was first diagnosed. And his parents had grabbed onto the hope of recovery. But, more than four years later, Anthony was still so distinguishable. What was wrong with him? It couldn't be the methods. They were "evidence based." One couldn't quibble with evidence. That was science. So, the deficit must be in Anthony himself. He wasn't trying hard enough. Or worse, he was too neurologically impaired to advance. Anthony's limitations alone were responsible for his slow progress. But there was still a little more time before the window closed. They had to press on!

His mom handed him his shirt and he pulled it over his head. "Good job, high five," his mom cheered in well-practiced tones. Anthony felt desperately frustrated.

Mom doesn't know I understand. I flap and flub and fail behind autism's mask and not even my own mom knows I am here praying to be able to communicate with her. I am here.

3

Bumbling

Anthony looked like an ordinary seven-year-old until he moved as autism dictated. Then, as his hands flapped like a flightless bird and his face hung flat and expressionless like a sagging shirt, any observant bystander could see that something wasn't quite right. It fell to his mom, or some other assistant, to help him not only get dressed but motor his way through all his activities each day. Even the simple tasks of putting on his shorts, shirt or his socks were not easy. His four-year-old brother could do it. "See Anthony, look. Like this," Gary would say. "No, it's backwards." "No, it's inside out." "No, the button is open."

Buttoning was out of the question. Anthony's fingers fumbled, like two left hands, weak and stumbling. He was not able to button his own jeans and he felt like he could no more see the front or the back of some of his t-shirts than a blind person. If the shirt had an obvious tag in the back, then Anthony could tell easily. But sometimes the tag was stamped onto the fabric, practically invisible to his gaze, or the t-shirts might confusingly have their graphics on the back of the shirt. Anthony needed his cues. If he missed them, if they were in the wrong place, he messed up. The ordinary activities his baby brother mastered easily were out of Anthony's reach. His visual processing system was garbled. He took in too much and he became overwhelmed. He missed things. His motor planning was unreliable. Just trying to sort it out took huge amounts of concentration and energy.

So many motor issues were off. His attempts at handwriting

and tracing looked illegible, like he was trying to hold a five-foot long pencil by its end. His control was poor. So were his pointing skills. If he was told to touch on demand an exact pinpoint or target he might misfire by an inch. Motor accuracy was a big problem for clumsy Anthony. He felt embarrassed by it and resented Gary for bragging so much about all his motor skills. His older brother, Mark, never did that. He seemed more sensitive to Anthony's frustration.

Even more annoying was that his body sometimes ignored his mind entirely. Then, it wasn't just clumsy. It was anarchy. In those moments, Anthony became a spectator to his body's whims. The body moved to some internal force that was not the mind's instruction and all Anthony could do was follow it.

Each time was a gamble. Get it right. Get it wrong. Autism decided for him. Anthony needed constant supervision to complete ordinary tasks. And every time he got dressed the struggle began anew.

"Anthony, pay attention. Your clothes are backwards. You can't go out looking that way," his mom complained, mostly to herself. She looked at Anthony and directed in a bright tone, "Turn shirt."

Anthony turned his shirt around with his mom's help, frustrated with himself and ashamed in front of Gary. Gary laughed. "Mommy, I'm little and Anthony is big, but I get dressed better than he does." Gary proudly showed her his buttoned pants and shirt in the right direction.

"Shhh, Gary," his mom said. "That's because Anthony doesn't understand what he's doing." Anthony made a loud noise, then he clumsily bumped into Gary's block tower making the blocks tumble in disarray to the floor.

"You big stupid head," Gary shrieked as he surveyed his ruined efforts. "Why don't you ever pay attention?" He was furious with Anthony. Gary was sure that it hadn't been an accident. Anthony bumbled across the room. Their mom told Gary it wasn't on purpose.

"He doesn't know better, honey," she consoled him.

Gary glared at his big brother. "He gets away with everything," he sulked.

It might seem obvious that some of Anthony's accidents were intentional, even a form of communication. Mom and Gary had hurt Anthony's feelings and Anthony hurt Gary's tower. But people looked at Anthony moving awkwardly and he sure looked like a guy who could have bumped the tower by accident, due to inattention, obliviousness or poor coordination. He also looked like a guy who might have touched it by pure impulsive instinct, as he did so many times, eager to see the blocks collapse in a loud boom of colors. What he didn't look was purposeful. Anthony might have been annoyed with his little brother and his own humiliating limitations. But he didn't look like it.

As was so often the case, only Anthony knew the real reason he did the things he did. Clumsy, impulsive, jealous, random. It could have been any of those. He really was clumsy, and he often was impulsive. That's when motor urges overrode his thinking. It happened when he grabbed colorful objects or ate sand or leapt into a pool fully clothed. Sometimes the block tower just needed to be pushed over.

Anthony understood compulsion only too well. One day, he came to realize that he wasn't the only one out there who watched helplessly as his body charged ahead without input from his mind. Mark had a classmate who suffered from Tourette's Syndrome. Mark heard him blurt out an offensive word in school even as he covered his mouth with his hands, trying to stop himself. Mark asked their mom about it.

"He has no control over it," his mom explained. "It's involuntary, like a sneeze, in a way."

The puzzling thing about Tourette's, she told Mark, is that the more the boy tries to resist the urge, the more compelled he becomes to act on it.

Mark was standing in the kitchen watching his mom cook dinner. He was in his soccer clothes. He had just come home from practice and hadn't removed his shin guards yet. He was eating a snack, too ravenous to wait for the meal. His face was still dirty with sweat. He had been thinking about the incident all day, troubled by it.

"How awful," Mark said. "He can't stop his mouth from swearing, like the thing he wants to do the least takes over."

"That's a profound insight, honey." His mom turned her eyes to Mark. Her oldest son, her one easy-going son.

Anthony heard the whole conversation. He was eavesdropping. Hanging by the doorway. Lurking, listening. He did that a lot. He identified with Mark's classmate. *I have body Tourette's, he thought. Sometimes my body obeys itself, not me. Then I have to follow it.*

How could anyone else know, observing Anthony, what force was driving his behavior in any given moment? They simply couldn't. And to make matters more confusing, from time to time Anthony's body did cooperate with his mind and do its bidding.

Well, it didn't really matter what was driving his actions since these inappropriate behaviors had to be corrected regardless. And anyway, the consensus was that Anthony lacked "theory of mind," or the ability to understand another's point of view, making clumsy revenge on Gary out of the question since acts of revenge required both insight and empathy. Specialists understood and explained that Anthony lived in a bubble, that he never imagined the feelings of others, or even realized they had any. Gary had a right to be frustrated, but his mom had also learned that he really couldn't blame his autistic brother. As she often told Gary, Anthony just didn't know better. As Anthony watched Gary's tower collapse and heard his brother yell he felt very satisfied. Gary's bragging, at least for the moment, was finished.

4
School

When the school bus pulled onto Pine Street, it was barely light out. Anthony was waiting at the curb with his mother. He was always the first passenger. The yellow mini-bus then wound its way through the suburbs to pick up four other boys who were going to special education classes, turning what would have been a fifteen-minute ride into an hour. His mom had no choice but to send Anthony on the long ride. His brothers went to other schools and the timing was too messed up for their mom to drop them all off. Mark's school wouldn't allow him to wait alone so long outside for the locked gates to open. Neither would Gary's, and he was too young to wait on his own anyway. His mom could have taken Anthony to school first. But his aide wasn't allowed to meet him there early because she wasn't paid for her work with Anthony until the school bell rang, and the school told Anthony's mother that they would not allow her to bring him to school late, after she dropped off his brothers. His dad, meanwhile, had to leave for work well before the school day began. So, for Anthony, the long, dull bus ride became his passage to a long, dull school day. This morning was no different.

Sitting on his bouncy, plastic seat alone, Anthony put his nose to the window. He listened to the other kids joke and share their games, but he might as well have been on the moon. None of the other kids had autism. They were in special education classes, so they rode the special bus to school, but they had little in common with a non-talking boy. Since no one approached him, and even if they had he wouldn't have been able to respond in a socially conventional way, Anthony turned to the kinesthetic world around him. His own hands made interesting shapes. His own mouth hummed and made interesting distractions. Perhaps he alone enjoyed his droning hum, but he did enjoy it and couldn't resist the pleasing, buzzing vibration in his throat. But lovelier than anything was the blur outside. The stationary pole and tree became streams of light and color when the bus passed them. Vanishing into the patterns of light, Anthony retreated from the chaos in the bus. If they didn't acknowledge him, *Who cares?* he thought. *I have my own private life to go to.*

To the other kids, Anthony probably didn't seem approachable. His face had a far-away gaze. His placid, expressionless features seemed void of intentionality. He didn't smile a greeting. He couldn't, of course, but they didn't have to know that to ignore him. He didn't talk. He moved his hands funny. He made annoying noises. He was kind of—well, totally— weird. Anthony laughed out loud at the vivid light show he alone saw. He didn't need them, he told himself.

When Anthony got to school, he entered his low-functioning autism class with Lily, his aide. Lily had long brown hair tied in a bun on the top of her head. She was wearing pink shorts and an old t-shirt with a college logo on it. She stood and twisted a loose loop of her hair before adding it to the bun. "High five, Anthony," she said unenthusiastically and moved her open hand in front of his face. She waited for him to touch her hand in return. Mrs. Lester, his buoyant teacher, came up and gave Anthony a hug in greeting. "Good morning, Anthony," she sang.

His class consisted of five other children with autism. Nearly all of them had no speech nor a means to communicate beyond the most basic wants. Only one student, the lone girl, could make words understandable. But her words were not sensible. She must have bored herself to tears saying the same phrases thousands of times, parroting television programs, singing song lyrics, echoing the last thing Mrs. Lester said. The staff regarded her as "higher functioning" because her speech allowed her to communicate basic replies. Not so for the silent boys, including Anthony. Babbling, grunting, moaning or shrieking, what passed for speech was unintelligible, except to the few people who were accustomed to their poorly articulated repertoire. Anthony's teacher knew that when Anthony verbalized, "ba-ba," it meant bathroom. "Sa-weh," meant sandwich. But other ears heard only gibberish. "How do you understand them?" the visiting principal remarked one day when observing the class. "I can't make heads or tails out of that,"

"Years of practice," Mrs. Lester answered drily.

This morning, his teacher was in a cheerful mood. She had loads of energy. "Put backpack in closet," she told Anthony in bright Pidgin English. Lily followed him to the closet, prompting him through the drill. "Sit on chair," Mrs. Lester told him next.

On plenty of days, Anthony's body wasn't cooperative. Then, he might wander randomly around the classroom, distracted by pink erasers that needed to be bitten or paper clips that needed to be untwisted, and proving to his teacher's dismay that he didn't understand the words backpack or closet. But on this day, Anthony succeeded. His backpack was in the closet. He sat on the chair. "Good job, Anthony!" Mrs. Lester beamed.

At school Anthony moved constantly between his two worlds. One could say that Autismland was his real world because he had built his sense of personhood there. Because his processing of sensory input was marred, that inner world was a bursting landscape of sound, sensation, color and movement. Anthony engaged in constant dialogue with it, trying to cope with the overwhelming amount of sensory information he took in. How could he not? On the outside, this looked like what his teachers called "behaviors." When he drowned in a beautiful moving string that waved tantalizingly or he paused to stare at dust illuminated in a beam of sunlight, or discovered the miracle of shadows moving while he walked, he was transfixed in the picture, his body intensely, magnetically thrilled, hands up and flapping. The real world of his teacher evaporated into the thrill of his senses. They had to pull him back.

"Hands quiet, Anthony," Mrs. Lester said, firm yet warm. But Anthony enjoyed the buzz immensely. Was there a reason to return to her interminable lessons of days of the week or colors? He might have enjoyed the lesson if it taught him something new, like learning the days in another language, or discussing color and light prisms, but, "What color? Blue. What color? Red," was not worth leaving the beauty of his interior panorama.

Mrs. Lester was a giant of a teacher, both literally and figuratively. She was nearly six feet tall with spiky grey hair, a former pole-vaulter. She loved her job, loved her students, loved Anthony, loved teaching and had lots of passion and enthusiasm for her work and hope for her students. Anthony loved her back. Her positive energy and personal warmth made her a comforting friend. It was lucky for Anthony that she had these attributes because otherwise he might not have been happy at all to go to school. Mrs. Lester kept her class moving and involved in many different learning activities. The problem was that they were all geared for students with language-processing disorders. Lessons were simple, mostly repetitive and designed to impart the most basic concepts. It was boring. Autismland beckoned appealingly.

Anthony sat with Lily at the table. He had a math worksheet in front of him. The same kind of worksheet he had last year and the year before, and was sure to get next year too. The equations were not hard: 1+3, 4+4, 5+2. He had to solve them and write the answer, but Lily felt Anthony didn't understand math. Mrs. Lester suspected he had no concept of what a number was, and Anthony had no real way to communicate his answers. This meant lots of mistakes and hand-over-hand prompts. As with his drills, school often reinforced the conclusion that Anthony didn't understand language, simple ideas and purposeful learning.

"Come on, Anthony," Lily cajoled, counting 4+4 on her fingers. "1, 2, 3, 4 plus 1, 2, 3, 4 is 8." She helped him trace the 8.

Oh duh, thought Anthony. Math came easily to him. No one knew. It was his own little secret. In his head, math was like a game. He multiplied double digits by single digits in his head. It amused him to figure out equations. It was mortifying to Anthony that people thought he was too confused or too intellectually behind to grasp that adding 1+1 made 2. He had the neurological capacity to understand sums at grade level and beyond, but to his instructors he appeared to be a confused simpleton.

Tug of war life. Parents, teachers and his team of professionals pulled him hard on one arm trying to get him to participate in their world—the educationally-boring, sensory-overwhelming real world—while Autismland grabbed his other arm to resist, to retreat, to get high on his own messed up neurology. Anthony had to make his way on neurological stepping-stones, hopping from stim, to terrible frustration, overwhelmed senses or boredom, and back to stim. Hop, hop, hop.

His real world was based on operant conditioning. In school, it earned Anthony lots of tokens. If he participated, if he answered questions or stayed in his chair or completed the simplified activity in his class, if he kept his hands quiet and didn't engage in his stims or self-stimulatory behaviors, Anthony got chips in green or blue. Ten chips won him a treat. This was the scientific strategy they used to get him to engage in their world. For Anthony, the true frustration was seeing that what they *wished* him to do and what he *could* do were miles apart.

Mrs. Lester took Anthony to the table to work individually on math skills. She spilled a small pile of wooden Popsicle sticks on the table and instructed him to give her one stick. He gave her a Popsicle stick. "Good job!" she exclaimed. Her spiky hair seemed to jab the air. She then asked for two Popsicle sticks. He again gave her one stick. Here was visible proof he didn't understand what a number was. "No, two," she said. She counted out loud, "One, two," as she picked up the two sticks. "You do it," she instructed. His hand again picked up just one Popsicle stick. Inside there was a fierce battle. Anthony's mind was so angry with his body. He felt humiliated once again. His triumphant body, as usual, had ignored his mind. It was programmed to pick up one. Period. The frustration Anthony felt was overwhelming. He flapped and vocalized for several minutes. Mrs. Lester watched with sympathy. It was so frustrating, she thought, for Anthony not to understand the lessons.

Intractable autism. That's what everyone believed. The system supported this outcome. In a low performance autism class filled with lots of hugs and lots of high-fives but missing academic expectation, little opportunity existed for Anthony to prove that his knowledge surpassed ABC, months of the year, days of the week and hot, cold or rainy weather. (He couldn't even convince people he understood *those* concepts.) He could not find his way out and no one thought to look and see if there might be more in him than what he showed behaviorally. Loneliness and fear were the natural outcomes. He felt so lonely. His ideas were deeply trapped in his mind, with no outlet. His hands couldn't hold his pencil to write. His mind lacked the means to order his hands to spell his thoughts. His mouth might as well have had no mind linked to it at all. All he had left was to mutter nonsensical sounds, unintelligible words or retreat to the sanctuary of Autismland.

The long ABA lessons, year after year, scared him. In a system that assumed he had a severe language processing disorder and interpreted his slow progress as being due to pervasive cognitive delays, Anthony could see no hope for himself. Inside, he absolutely knew he was intelligent. He already could read. He yearned so much to be able to express his thoughts and to let people know how smart he was, but his motor system refused to let him. For Anthony, the fact that he was being treated for a language processing input disorder, a disability he didn't have, left his actual disability, the breakdown in his body's ability to receive and act on instructions from his mind, unexplored by professionals. He got hours of professional treatment every day, but he knew that his treatments actually prevented him from truly being helped. He knew that the hours of drilling, in words he already understood, satisfied everyone except him, because everyone believed he was receiving the most and the best he could get. This was the heartbreaking, horrible fear he tried to flee—that he might never, ever be able to show anyone who Anthony was, that he would live his whole life one-sided, spoken to but not answering, discussed but not able to dispute, stuck in his own under-responsive body forever, never able to share his thoughts. And that is loneliness.

5

Recess

The bell rang. It was time for recess with the normals. Anthony's classmates and their aides stood in their corner of the playground while the other students played in the rest of the yard. Some of his classmates climbed on the equipment, some stimmed, some stood alone, and a few had volunteer motherly neurotypicals to lead them around by the hand each recess. Anthony enjoyed watching movement, so cars in motion, feet in motion, kids in motion, shadows in motion, balls in motion, even mouths in motion could bring him swirling sensorally. His coping strategy disengaged him from others.

"Look at him," one boy laughed and pointed as Anthony flapped his hands in excitement after watching his ball roll across the playground yard. "Why does he do that? It's so weird." In response to comments like these, Anthony could only flap even more, this time because he was upset. He had no ability to scold the other boys or even to let them know that he heard them. Because his hands were linked to his stress system neurologically, his only available response was to do even more intensely what they had mocked to begin with.

These daily encounters on the playground reminded Anthony that he couldn't chase or joke with peers the way he would have liked. If a mind wishes and the body refuses to obey, what can a child do? No matter how much Anthony wished to have a conversation with another boy, he could not. Years of boring, frustrating speech therapy had not brought him closer to being able to converse. A few single, unintelligible words do not make a conversation.

In terms of socially interacting on the playground with typical children, the stated goal of his entire educational team, Anthony was stymied. Sometimes he found himself high-fived and spoken to like a toddler, led around by the hand by the eight- year-old girl volunteer, but that wasn't really interacting in the way he would have liked. He had to follow her lead, but he preferred not to. What he really wished to do was play ball with the typical boys, to be able to play and joke like them. It was frustrating to know that he couldn't. His messed-up motor connections always interfered with his plans. There was no chance he could organize his body to participate in their ball game. It would have been as realistic as asking those boys to play by swimming in the air and to communicate through telepathy. That's when Anthony dreamed of escaping to his mind's respite—the lights, the patterns, the shining loveliness. To professionals it looked as though he had no interest in other kids, that he was infantile and only cared about his stims, but that was wrong. Anthony had to cope in his own way, the way that was available to him, putting frustrating, painful feelings into a box. The escape was always there, beckoning him. The hard job was resisting.

Anthony raised his hands again to flap. He had to let his frustration out and his hands were the outlet. They were hardwired to his frustration sensors, his excited sensors and his boredom sensors. While his face was void of facial expressions, his waving hands conveyed feelings. They were like autism Morse code, flapping to the dot-dash of his emotions. Lily said, "Hands quiet," for the hundredth time. She looked at the playground inattentively.

He constantly practiced not flapping because Lily told him, "Hands quiet," over and over. After each command, he paused for an instant and resumed. Lily was a person in the wrong profession. She had no passion, no interest, no creativity and no brains. Anthony smelled her lazy indifference like a shark smelled blood in the water and it made him wage war on her. He had power in the only way powerless people have. He practiced passive resistance against her. Lily couldn't figure out why Anthony cooperated so readily with Mrs. Lester and ignored her so often, but the reason was pretty simple. Mrs. Lester was caring and loving and he liked her, while Lily was lazy and indifferent and he disliked her. It never occurred to Lily that Anthony understood what he was doing since she assumed he had no comprehension of cause and effect, let alone language. Mrs. Lester had to intervene often in his undeclared war.

Of course, the biggest loser in his war was Anthony himself. The worse he behaved the more he proved to them that he was not aware of things. Battling Lily made her miserable on the job, which was momentarily satisfying. On the other hand, battling her made her disinterest grow. It seemed that she could not care less. Useless in helping Anthony function, she focused instead on policing his hand flapping. That was her job. "Hands quiet, Anthony. Hands quiet, Anthony. Hands quiet, Anthony." She was the 'hands-quiet' police patrol. She would also be with him for many more months until the school year ended. He hoped he would get someone better next year.

Mrs. Lester called to Anthony, "Come, Anthony, climb to the slide." She led him to the ladder. He stopped flapping and began climbing to please her. Lily gaped. He climbed around on the playground equipment until the students were herded back to class to study "vocabulary"—by watching the same alphabet video Mrs. Lester always played.

"A is for apple," it droned. "B is for book." Anthony knew

the film by heart. He heard it in his head on the bus, in his sleep, that same boring recitation of letters. *Help*, he thought. *A is for agony. B is for bored. C is for cut it out. D is for dumb*. He mocked the film in his mind, amusing himself with his own version of each letter. *P is for pointless. Q is for quit*. He started laughing when he got to the letter 'R'. *R is for rescue me*.

"Why are you laughing?" Lily asked. "Watch movie. No laugh."

Me Tarzan. You dumb, Anthony thought. He laughed more.

"He stims so much during this movie," Lily remarked.

6

Dr. Hagerty

Anthony's parents sat listening to Dr. William Hagerty, Anthony's well-known psychiatrist, who was responsible for his medication planning. His mother was weeping and his father wore his serious expression, the one he used to mask his pain.

"His ego is not integrated," Hagerty told them in his supercilious voice. He was droning on about his favorite subject again—that Anthony had no empathy, no imagination, no idea that others existed. "He never thinks of what his behavior looks like, or how he impacts others. Why should he care if people are inconvenienced or have to fix his messes after him?"

Dr. Hagerty was known as one of the country's most experienced and influential child psychiatrists specializing in autism. In ABA circles, the man was a god. There was a famous tale about his landmark epiphany, which had occurred almost five decades ago. The story had become a kind of legend, repeated by Hagerty's acolytes all over the world.

As a psychiatry intern, Dr. Hagerty had been watching the repeated errors of a young boy confined to a state hospital. The nurse there directed the boy to wipe his face with a napkin, but the boy could not follow even simple commands. He picked up his spoon. That's when Dr. Hagerty's light bulb came on. As he often told it, he realized immediately that the boy lacked the ability to differentiate between the two different *words*. If I can drill him, he thought, perhaps I can make him understand. He sat next to the boy and placed a napkin and a spoon in front of him. Looking sternly at the boy, he said, "Pick up the napkin." The boy picked up the napkin. "Good. Good," said Dr. Hagerty. Then he switched the places of the napkin and the spoon, and commanded, "Pick up the spoon." The boy's hand shot to the spoon. "Now, pick up the napkin." The boy's hand moved, again reaching for the same location. He picked up the spoon. "Wrong," Hagerty told him, waving each object in front of the boy. "Look, napkin. Spoon. Napkin. Spoon." The boy sat mute and inattentive. He stared at the ceiling. Suddenly Dr. Hagerty noticed a box of raisins and brought them to the table. "Touch spoon," he commanded again. The boy touched the spoon. Dr. Hagerty put a raisin in his mouth. "Touch spoon," he said again, switching the positions of the spoon and napkin. The boy touched the spoon again and got another raisin. "Touch spoon," Dr. Hagerty ordered again and again. In a mere ten minutes Dr. Hagerty had taught this boy the word spoon.

The child had been institutionalized since the age of five. But from that day on, as Dr. Hagerty recounted in just about every lecture for the next fifty years, using this strategy Dr. Hagerty taught him to recognize more than a hundred words, including some verbs and adjectives. He even learned to perform some basic tasks, like washing his own hair. He eventually worked in the kitchen wiping tables. The hospital, Hagerty said, had initially concluded that the boy had an IQ of 30. "Lucky for him, it was his language processing that interfered with his comprehension, not his IQ," Hagerty would tell each audience of adoring students, "and lucky for me, he liked raisins."

The students laughed on cue.

Language processing deficiency was to blame. That was Dr. Hagerty's message. Overcoming it could turn permanent stagnation into thriving. "We may not know why some kids take off and some languish," he often concluded. "Probably some just have too severe a language disorder to enable them to overcome such pervasive deficit. But many can and do learn."

Dr. Hagerty shifted in his seat, his hefty frame causing the chair to groan audibly. Clearly, he had filed Anthony in the stagnant column.

"It will be a long journey to help him understand that humans are others with rights too," he told them.

"How can that be?" sobbed Anthony's mom. "I notice glimmers of more in him."

"Good," Dr. Hagerty said. "Glimmers are useful. But let's train him to control his impulses, because he does not respond to insight."

It was an interesting conversation to Anthony. He paced the room, fiddling with a plastic bead necklace he found in a toy box in the corner. He looked lost in his own world. Why not? He was nervous. His body was restless. Dr. Hagerty had just given his parents incorrect information about his potential and there was nothing he could do to set it right. The movement of the dangling, dancing beads took him straightaway to relief. They made Dr. Hagerty vanish. "Stop, Anthony," his dad said. "Put down beads." Anthony ignored him. Why should he stop?

Dr. Hagerty was looking at him, pity on his face. He watched Anthony front to back, dancing on his toes, flapping his hands, waving beads. "He needs more structure," he concluded. "How many hours of ABA is he getting currently?"

Anthony's mom listed off his torturous itinerary. "Three hours every day after school, four days a week. Speech and OT the other day. Social skills group. On weekends, he gets eight more hours."

He was making progress, she told Dr. Hagerty, just slowly.

"Hmmm," Dr. Hagerty replied, exhaling slowly. It was a dubious sound, almost accusatory.

Anthony noticed his mother hunched in her chair, her body aching with sorrow. Suddenly, he ran to her and gave her a hug from behind, around her neck.

"Oh, Anthony, my sweet boy," his mom cried.

"That isn't quite a hug," Dr. Hagerty said calmly, informing her. "He is stimming on you. Does he do that often?"

"Not really," his mom answered, deflated. "I thought he was hugging me."

"It is a hug of sorts, of course," Dr. Hagerty said dismissively. "But not a hug hug." He pushed the point hard. It seemed obvious to him that this mother was in some denial, though the father appeared to have recognized the situation. "He is stimming on you like he hugs that stuffed animal," he pointed loosely to a pile of therapy toys discarded on the floor near the toy box in the corner of his office. "He gets proprioceptive feedback."

What hope was there for Anthony to show this expert that he had theory of mind, that he recognized that his mom was sorrowful and needed consolation and that his body had actually obeyed him in that moment? Even Anthony's hugs were pathologized.

"You mean to say that was completely random, then?" Anthony's father asked, incredulous.

"How does he perform on his emotions drills?" Dr. Hagerty countered. "Is he able to consistently distinguish the different emotions?"

The answer was not really. He often messed those up when drilled on photos. Happy face. Sad face. Angry face.

Dr. Hagerty listened, then issued his verdict. Anthony was

likely stimulated in some way by the intensity of emotion he perceived. But that didn't mean he understood what it was. "Whether you were laughing, crying or angry makes no difference to his perception," he explained. "It comes in as a blur. He probably hugs you like this in random moments, I imagine."

"Yes," Anthony's mom conceded, "but so do my other sons."

Dr. Hagerty smiled like a sphinx. His clinical training told him to back off. He was threatening the mother's defenses. It wasn't time to puncture her false hope. Over time, harsh truths would no doubt pop her balloon, but that could be years away. The window of opportunity for Anthony to make more progress was still marginally open, so let her have her hope. He shook their hands to end the session and called Anthony's name to say good-bye. Anthony hopped around the room, immersed in his inner escape. In Dr. Hagerty's eyes, Anthony seemed a lost soul, a half-lived life, a person with no personhood. The doctor shrugged. These kinds of cases were challenging. He opened the door and Anthony ran from the room, dashing wildly for the exit.

"Anthony, stop!" his mother yelled, as Dr. Hagerty observed solicitously from his office door.

"He is so arrogant," Anthony's father grumbled once they were in the car. "He treats us like we're ignoramuses."

What about me, Dad? Anthony screamed in his head. *He may not treat you like you're smart, but he thinks I'm barely human*! Anthony flapped the entire way home, bothering his parents with his loud and guttural vocalizations.

As soon as the car came to a stop in the driveway, Anthony ran for the door. In a bin in the family room, he found his pile of sensory toys and held them tightly. He rubbed the bumpy ball hard against his hand, observing the pain with some pleasure. He hated doing the bidding of his primal compulsions. On the other hand, he liked feeling that his hand could feel. Most of the time, Anthony's body was like a kind of phantom. Often, he barely felt where his body was in space. Rubbing his hand on the ball made his hand feel alert. He wondered if that was how a normal hand felt. He ran to his room and jumped on his bed. "Stop jumping, Anthony! No jump! No jump!" his mom yelled. To herself she muttered, "We cannot afford another mattress and box spring."

Anthony needed to move badly. His body was filled with energy and tension. He felt coiled up, about to burst, like a kernel of popcorn on the brink. Perhaps the source of the tension was the horrible resentment he felt. Dr. Hagerty lectured at the respected state university and travelled internationally, presenting speeches on autism. He was exceptionally expensive. Anthony knew his parents wanted to move to a new house but couldn't afford it. He wondered if their sacrifice went to buying Dr. Hagerty's bad advice. He raced randomly around his home in hyperactive and impulsive spurts of tense energy, touching everything, throwing cushions to the floor, making a mess. His mother took him by the hand and led him onto their mini trampoline. There he could channel his energy and he jumped and jumped and jumped his frustration out.

Anthony was only seven years old. He obviously had no PhD or MD degree like Dr. Hagerty did. But he knew some things that Dr. Hagerty didn't. Anthony often longed to tell Dr. Hagerty that the theories and insights he relayed to Anthony's parents were incorrect. He imagined going up to him and yelling, *I was hugging my mom, you jerk*! Dr. Hagerty truly had no clue that Anthony understood language. He had no clue that the reason Anthony was not talking was because of a neurological impediment that stopped Anthony's body from obeying his mind. He had no clue that the symptoms he observed so intensely, the uncontrolled movements, the flaps, the noises, were a burden to Anthony, that Anthony couldn't stop them any more than Dr. Hagerty could hold in his hiccups.

This high-end psychiatrist held power over Anthony, no question. He influenced other professionals and guided Anthony's parents in their thinking. He could even persuade his mom and dad that a hug that they both observed was just a random stim. He, and many other experts, it seemed to Anthony, were like prison guards marching outside his door, loaded with good intentions and meager expectations. Anthony longed for escape, but he had to break through the twelve-foot-high theory barrier that the guards had constructed. Their insights and benevolent, patronizing programming served only to lock Anthony into a life of doing the least he could demonstrate.

7

ABA

After school was over, Anthony came home to a rotating crew of behaviorists who worked with him on drills. The professional who had the most power over Anthony's day-to-day life was Natasha Olsen. Though he only saw her once a week, when his entire ABA team gathered in her office to review his daily performance, her fingerprints were on every lesson his ABA team forced on him, every day. It was Natasha who devised the curriculum of discrete trials and operant conditioning that the team of behaviorists had to follow precisely. He left school early on supervisory days.

The lessons were numerous—crafted to address Anthony's pervasive deficits. There were drills that used flashcard pictures to teach Anthony how to identify simple objects, and more drills to train him to follow basic commands. "Jump." "Turn around." "Touch your nose." These escalated in complexity. "Wipe the table." "Wipe your nose." Simple drills to identify one object, like "chair" or "car," built towards entire categories of objects, such as furniture or vehicles. The behaviorists taught nouns first. Verbs would follow, and adjectives, much more challenging conceptually, would come even later, after Anthony mastered the earlier concepts. It all depended upon how quickly Anthony progressed. To demonstrate progress, he had to point to the correct flashcard.

The single most important concept in Natasha's grand scheme was teaching labels. Like Annie Sullivan putting Helen Keller's hand under running water and fingerspelling "w-a-t-e-r," onto her hand over and over until Helen gleaned that "w-a-t-e-r" and the wet stuff were the same, Anthony's behaviorists drilled him again and again, making him point to flashcard photos of doors, tables, flowers, pencils, spoons, potatoes. Thanks to the data the behaviorists collected and entered into the logbooks, Natasha knew, at every weekly supervision, exactly how Anthony had performed on each drill. She knew exactly how much he knew.

Every day, Anthony worked at home with his team of ABA behaviorists. Today it was Nina, but she was easily swapped out for Alyssa or Charlotte. They were all longhaired, good-looking, fresh out of college, brimming with enthusiasm and surety in their methods. Nina greeted Anthony, "Hey tiger, how are you?" She tickled his stomach and gave him a high-five. "High-five," she chirped. "How was school today?" she asked Anthony's mom.

"Nothing to report, really," His mom answered. "Anthony seems a bit tired. Not sure if he'll give much effort today."

"In that case, we'd better get some motivating reinforcers," Nina said with perky energy. She looked in the pantry for favorite food treats and filled a bowl with broken up pretzel bits. "Perfect," she said in her energetic, singsong way, "working for pretzels."

Just then, Gary entered. "Hi Nina. Want to see what I made in pre-school? Look!" He put a crayon scribble on the table.

"You are such a good artist, Gary. Wow!" Nina admired Gary's work. Gary told her what he had learned in pre-school. She praised him. Gary loved the attention he got from the behaviorists. And any time Gary spent showing his accomplishments to Nina was time Anthony could steal to vanish, to escape mentally in preparation for the three hours of drilling he was about to undergo. He had a tried and true method. While Gary distracted Nina, Anthony went to his room, picked up his iPad, opened it to his go-to, a cartoon he always went to for escape and had watched a hundred times before. He brought it right up to his face. It touched his nose. He turned his eyes sideways and peered intensely out of the corner of his eye. Immediately Anthony was teleported into sensory worlds that put him into a mindless state. His body pulsated internally and he heard nothing to disturb him. That is, until Nina found him.

"Hi, kiddo. Time to sit down. iPad all done." She made the sign language symbol for 'all done' and shook her hands. "No more iPad. Sit down at table." She took the iPad. "All done," she repeated and flicked her hands. Anthony got up and walked to the table.

Okay, three hours, he thought to himself, *to prove that I'm stupid. Only I'm not.*

Anthony was used to it. Under Natasha's guidance, he'd had approximately 5,000 hours of these lessons over the years. Labeling drills. Expressive drills. Touch this. Touch that. Do this!

"Touch po-ta-to." Nina sang her commands in an animated voice. Anthony looked at the array of flashcards, this time a book, a tennis ball, a horse, a plate and a baked potato covered in sour cream. The theory was if he touched the potato picture correctly every time Nina asked, then everyone could be certain that he knew the word for potato. That he knew the *concept* of potato. (Though perhaps not the concept of a raw potato, or French fries, or potato salad. Potato-ness, the ability to generalize potato in all its forms, would come later in a different drill). But if Anthony only touched the potato flashcard correctly half the time, then he demonstrated that he wasn't quite sure what a potato was. If that happened, he'd need to practice more until the label was mastered.

Nina and the other behaviorists also drilled Anthony with flashcard pictures of his mom, dad, Gary, Mark, his grandparents, neighbors, themselves, Natasha, teachers, family friends and other therapists. Since Anthony couldn't always even distinguish a potato from something totally different, like a pillow, he certainly needed help learning to distinguish his mom from four-year-old Gary, his male adaptive PE teacher or a random stranger. Not surprising, really, since Anthony sometimes took the hand of unknown women in the supermarket, surprising them and embarrassing his mom. "Does he really think that's me?" his mom fretted. "I'm standing right here."

The behaviorists drilled Anthony to recognize feelings. They displayed pictures of exaggerated facial expressions—a sad face, an angry face, a surprised face and a happy face—and ordered him to identify the emotions correctly by touching the correct flashcard. Then there was the expressive emotions drill, where they commanded him to mimic the facial expressions. It was very difficult for Anthony to make the desired expressions at will and his imitations were not convincing. A grimace for a smile, the same grimace for an angry face, an open mouth for surprised, a pushed out lower lip for sad. He tried his best but there was no animation. Most of the time his face was just flat.

In another exercise, Nina instructed Anthony to build a tower identically copying what she had just constructed from a few multi-colored blocks. And in another, meant to reinforce his eye contact skills, he stared into her eyes for thirty seconds following the command, "Look at me," while a timer kept count. His ABA team amassed reams of paper and multiple binders filled with data on his performance, deficits, progress, or lack of progress. The drills and logbooks defined his life. When he made mistakes, as he often did, his days were also filled with the word, "no." Each and every time Anthony gave the wrong answer in a drill he would hear them say, "No, try again," in the singsong, off-pitch, so-called "neutral no" of ABA artificial speak. Perhaps no one else on earth, except an ABA instructor, said "no" just like that. And because it sounded odd and not mad or frustrated, just odd, it was deemed to be "neutral" and somehow clinical. *That's a laugh*, thought Anthony. *Neutral. Ha-ha.*

He sat down at the little table in his bedroom where he worked with his behaviorists. Nina readied the flashcards for Anthony's receptive labels drill. She spread five cards on the table so that Anthony had to scan a broad area. One of them was a lemon. "Touch le-mon," she enunciated slowly and carefully. She stared straight ahead. In her supervisory reviews, Natasha had noticed how sensitive Anthony was to glances or the slightest hint. If a behaviorist's glance led him to a card, Natasha considered it a cheat that would skew the data. The team members had all been trained to avoid this. Sometimes they covered part of their faces with a piece of paper. This time, Nina stared straight at the wall like an unblinking Barbie doll. Anthony grabbed the card with a lemon. "Good job, Anthony. High five." She gave him a pretzel crumb. Anthony swallowed the pretzel bite and reached for the bowl to take more. "No, no," Nina said firmly. She moved the bowl away and shuffled the cards around to put them in different places on the table. Autism three-card Monte.

"Touch banana," she sang out. Anthony's hand touched the lemon.

Damn my hand! Flap flap flap.

"No, try again. Touch ba-na-nuh," she enunciated with excruciating care. His hand went to the lemon again.

Why is my hand doing this today? Down in the logbook, Nina wrote the data. *Oh no*! Anthony thought. *They think I can't tell the difference between a lemon and a banana.*

The reason Anthony touched the lemon had nothing to do with comprehension. It was true he was clumsy and he had terrible motor accuracy. He also had poor ability to tell his body to listen to him, but it was more than that. His hand was insisting on touching that lemon. It wasn't listening to his brain. It happened often and it skewed their data.

Nina was perplexed because Anthony had mastered both lemon and banana in previous drills. She wondered if maybe he had relied on the color to prompt him in those earlier drills. Maybe he was confused by having cards of two yellow fruits. She tried again.

"Touch lemon," she commanded and Anthony touched the lemon correctly. Shuffle shuffle. "Touch ba-na-nuh." Anthony watched his hand move to the lemon picture again and he screamed inside.

Why the hell is my hand insisting on lemon today? he fretted. *My hand is driving me nuts! I hate my disobedient body!*

The logbook didn't lie. Anthony often got the answers wrong and the data reflected that.

Nina never seemed to wonder whether motor compulsions or body control issues might be to blame. Her evidence proved that Anthony had trouble distinguishing between the lemon and the banana. That was *scientific* proof. The data had the answers. Nina noticed how Anthony scowled or flapped his hands when he made mistakes. "He just hates to be wrong," she told Anthony's mother. "It's really interesting how upset he gets." Anthony rolled his eyes in his mind at this comment. He imagined some force taking over her body and causing her to flub all her own tests in school and figured she might get upset by that.

Unfortunately for Anthony he had no motor ability to communicate that message so the moment his session was over he found another outlet, his favorite photo of a cougar. It was a close-up photo of the big cat's face. Its brown eyes sparkled intensely in light streams, lines and colors. Anthony opened his book about felines and from well-practiced motor memory found the exact page he needed. He stared intently at the cougar's eyes and it gave him a rush of peace. Intense chills ran through his body. Anthony momentarily forgot about lemons and bananas and how much he loathed his disobedient body.

"I think we need to confiscate this book," Nina observed. "It's a fixation."

8

Show Time

Once a week, Anthony had to attend a supervision session with his behaviorists and Natasha. The supervisions were the most despised appointments in his schedule. They left him no room to escape into his internal world. Natasha scrutinized him every moment and noticed every one of his flubs. He felt like a dolphin in a marine park or a dog performing tricks. Like them, he had learned to work for bits of food and praise. But the sad truth was the dolphin and the dog did better than Anthony because they had no neurological impediments interfering with their performance. The team and his mom were gathered to witness Anthony's humiliation and await tweaks in his programming. Each discussion of his flubs drove him up the wall.

"Okay, how has this week gone?" Natasha began, logbook on her lap, legs tightly coiled, over the knee and then at the ankle. "Receptive labels…looks like we've had some issues. Have you tried replacing the card with something that isn't yellow?" Everyone nodded. Natasha called out, "Who wants to go first?" Nina volunteered and took Anthony to the worktable in the center of the room. He sat at the table. Anxiety filled his body.

Which way today? Does the dice roll on crazy body or does it listen to me? I can't take another week of lemon/banana. He looked at the table, cards arrayed in front of him.

"Touch ball," Nina commanded. His hand easily touched the ball picture. "Good job," she chuckled. "Touch window." Anthony brought his finger perfectly to the window. He felt relieved. This might be a good day. "Touch banana." There they were, the pictures of banana and lemon.

Oh no, he panicked. *Don't touch the lemon*, he pleaded with his hand. He watched in horror as his disobedient hand went straight to the wrong picture.

"Reverse them," Natasha suggested. He flubbed again. "Put the banana picture closer to him," she barked. This time, he touched the banana correctly but when the cards' positions were reversed, his hand once again went to the wrong card. "Hmmm," the expert pondered, "try putting an 'L' and a 'B' on the pictures to help him differentiate."

Tweak after tweak, the suggestions flew, as the women discussed Anthony, analyzing the perplexing riddle of his incorrect answers. Shame engulfed him. Why did his body hate him so? Finally, Natasha stopped telling her team about Anthony and the lemon banana crisis. "Okay, let's stop plugging away on that for now," Natasha decided. "Let's try something totally different. How about the eye contact drill? Nina stayed in her seat, took out her timer, set it for thirty seconds, started it, and stared intently into Anthony's eyes. This was supposed to make Anthony more comfortable with eye contact. It was the drill he detested most.

Real natural. People always look at each other like that, he thought sarcastically.

"Look at me," Nina sang out. Autism staring contest.

And so, they plugged away through all the drills. Natasha took notes, suggested, decreed. Anthony flubbed, filled with self-loathing, rage, self-pity. They always joked about how much he hated to be wrong, but his flat, expressionless face made it hard for them to read the pain buried within him.

*Maybe I need to get **them** some flashcards so they can learn to recognize **my** feelings*, Anthony grumbled inside.

"Autistic people do have emotions," a child psychologist told his mother years earlier, as if it were an extraordinary revelation. One thing was certain: his ABA team sure couldn't see them.

9

Mark Sees

Anthony's mom liked reading to her boys. She read the Henry Huggins books because little Gary could follow the humorous stories, and older Mark liked them too. Anthony's mom didn't expect Anthony to listen to the stories, let alone understand them, but she found that including him was good practice for sitting politely. To keep him occupied as she read, she brought Anthony a pile of sensory toys. He had his bumpy balls, his mushy squeeze toys and his soft stuffed animals on hand to keep him calm and prevent him from wandering off.

They had moved on to his mother's childhood favorites, the Laura Ingalls Wilder's *Little House* books about her family's days as pioneering homesteaders in the American Midwest. It was thrilling for Anthony to hear the stories of their struggles with wildfires, crop failure, loneliness, horrible weather and other dangers. And they still endured, facing even more adventures. In one book, Pa got caught in an extreme blizzard on his way back home and somehow made it through, huddled in a snow cave. Anthony's mom read about the father's struggle to survive, alone, freezing and starving. She read about the fears of his family, waiting at home, thinking he might be dead, and Pa's own worries that his wife and young daughters would not survive on the homestead without him. Gary was upset. "Is he okay?" he asked, over and over.

"It happened more than a hundred years ago, dummy," Mark said contemptuously. Mom chided him for insulting his little brother. She explained how it was difficult for the pioneers to find their way in whiteout conditions. People sometimes got lost and froze to death just a few yards from their homes. To tend to their animals, they would tie a rope to their house and hold on to it to help them find their way back from the barn. She read on. Pa was huddled in his cave, starving, but he found some hard candy in his pocket that he had purchased in town for his children. It kept him alive. The passage was so vivid that Anthony was overcome with anxiety. Tossing his sensory toys onto the floor he ran out of the room.

"Where did he go?" Gary stared at the empty hallway.

"He seemed scared," Mark observed.

"He doesn't understand," Gary remarked. "Why is he scared?"

Their mom explained what Dr. Hagerty had often pointed out, that Anthony picks up on the intensity of other people's emotions. "It was scary and emotional," she said. "He must have felt that somehow without understanding it."

Mark looked skeptical. "Mom," he said, "I think he was upset by what he heard."

"I don't think so, honey," his mom said with affection and a hint of sadness. "He can't even follow a simple instruction. I mean, I tell him to get a fork and he gets a spoon. I tell him to close the door and he closes his toy box." She sighed. "I wish you were right, Mark, truly. There's nothing I want more than for Anthony to understand."

"Read more, Mommy," Gary ordered.

Mark held up his hand, signaling them to wait. Then he trotted down the hall looking for his brother.

A few moments later, they could hear Mark calling. When mom and Gary got to Anthony's bedroom, they found him sitting in the middle of his bed, completely hidden under his blanket. In Anthony's mind, he was struggling alone in a cave, like Pa.

"What is he doing?" Gary squealed.

"I think he's scared," Mark insisted.

"He's never done anything like this before," his mom said. She sounded dubious, and unsure.

"Well, maybe he's never been scared before," Mark said, his voice rising. "He doesn't get stories like this usually. Just cardboard books." His mom pulled an idea out of her bag of tricks. If Anthony absorbed the moods around him, the solution was simple. Change the mood. She pretended to laugh, pulling the blanket off Anthony. He pulled it back on.

"Silly boy," she said, trying to tickle him. "Book all done." She made the sign language gesture for 'all done.' Mark was staring intently.

"Mom, he's not stupid!" Mark suddenly yelled. He jumped in front of his mom and crouched next to the blanket-covered lump that was his brother. "Anthony," he said softly and firmly. "I know Pa is okay. Come out and we can finish the chapter. You'll see."

"Mark, stop," his mom told him, irritated. "He doesn't process what you're saying." Mark ignored her.

"Come on out Anthony," he coaxed, "and I'll sit with you." Suddenly Anthony pulled off the blanket. He loved Mark, intuitive, respectful, kind Mark. Mark saw what no one else did. He saw potential in his brother. His mom stared. She felt confused watching Mark lead Anthony down the hall by the hand. What just happened? she wondered. Had Anthony understood or had he just responded to Mark's kindness and his offered hand? Autism was so perplexing. Her eyes saw glimmers. But the data didn't lie, did it?

10

OT

Haley put Anthony into a rotating swing, coiled it tightly and let him spin round and round. "He is seeking proprioceptive input," she remarked to Anthony's mom. "His brain is seeking input because his vestibular system is under-developed."

In the litany of drills and therapies foisted on him, coming here to see Haley was definitely not the worst. She was Anthony's occupational therapist. The room was cavernous, filled with all the tools of the trade to supposedly jiggle, twirl and swing Anthony into sensory alertness. Anthony could have fun here. He just had to outmaneuver her. It wasn't always easy.

"I think he might get dizzy" Anthony's mom remarked.

"You know," Haley answered, "I have never seen a kid with autism get dizzy. They have the opposite response that you would. Putting people with autism on a rotating swing calms them and helps them to work better."

Anthony's mom smiled a crooked smile. "He would make a good astronaut then," she joked.

"How could he be an astronaut?" Haley looked confused. Anthony rolled his eyes internally. He got off the swing and staggered to the wall. The room was spinning and he felt queasy. Perhaps he was one of the few people with autism who couldn't spin indefinitely.

"He seems much calmer," Haley said. "Come Anthony, let's do it again." She took him by the hand. Anthony pulled his hand from hers and tried to run away. She put him onto the rotating swing again. He jumped off. "He's so oppositional today," Haley laughed. Anthony flapped his hands. How else was he supposed to communicate his wish to not nauseate himself again? Haley insisted on returning to the spinning swing, but Anthony ran to the trampolines. Haley shrugged. He'd get proprioceptive feedback there too, so why not just let him?

Anthony loved the trampolines. He flew. He was free. He jumped with Haley, throwing himself onto the huge trampoline on his knees, his bottom and his tummy. Every bounce and impact delivered a message to his brain, helping it understand where his body was in space. It was feedback he needed. It was also enormously entertaining, an exercise he could do well despite his clumsiness and poor motor planning. After a few minutes, Haley was perspiring and breathing hard. "Okay, Anthony, all done," she called. "All done trampoline." She walked him to the monkey bars. Anthony tried to escape back to the trampoline. "He is really in need of that input today," Haley laughed.

The trampoline is fun! Monkey bars are not fun! Anthony shouted internally. In Haley's world, everything he did had a cause. Vestibular, proprioceptive, seeking this or that. Yes, he got feedback from the trampoline, but couldn't something in his life simply be fun?

Anthony's physical limitations created a lot of frustration in his life. Once his father took him to a t-ball team for disabled kids to try to expose him to some regular kid activity. On the surface, Anthony looked like the least impacted participant there. Most of the players were pushed around the bases in wheelchairs, or blind and tracking a beeping ball, or severely motor impaired in some other noticeable way. But it was Anthony who had the most difficulty following the ball and keeping his focus on the game. As for hitting the ball? That was out of the question. Standing far out in the outfield gave Anthony a chance to return to Autismland, so when a ball finally did come near him all he did was flap his hands as it rolled by. The coaches dragged him around the bases shouting encouragement. They didn't know how to engage him. Anthony had shown nothing but resistance and disinterest in the t-ball league. He went three times. Then his dad gave up. But the trampoline he could do. He could jump. He loved jumping this way. It was pure enjoyment.

Haley coaxed a reluctant Anthony away from the trampoline to hang on the monkey bars. This was really hard for him. Anthony's arms were puny and weak. Grabbing the bars hurt his hands and his grasp was loose. After just a few seconds, he let go. His fingers felt like baseball gloves. They had no traction hanging on the bar, his useless body pulling him down like a bag of soggy potatoes. *I'm potato-boy*, thought Anthony. He hated his motor system and his weak and klutzy body. Haley made him try again and he let go immediately. *Why even try?* he moped inside.

"He has low muscle tone," Haley casually observed.

"What do you mean?" his mom asked. She was in her own exercise clothes from a hasty workout in front of the TV, the most she could muster. She followed Haley and her son around blearily, getting some pleasure from Anthony's obvious joy when he jumped and wincing at his difficulty on the monkey bars.

"He is soft muscled." Haley touched Anthony's right arm and pointed loosely at his untoned belly.

"Won't they get stronger?" his mom asked in surprise.

"They may," Haley said, "but it's hard for him. He has weak core development, minimal muscle mass in his chest and arms." She listed his deficits as Anthony listened.

Diagnosis: weak and unfit. Whatever can we do? Option One: work on physical fitness. Option Two: observe that someone has low muscle tone. The end.

"Can he work out, then?" Anthony's mom inquired.

"I think he has to be motivated to do that," Haley answered. "How does he respond to exercise?"

Anthony's mom recited her son's delights. Jumping. Swimming, Splashing in water. Even riding a scooter. Good, Haley responded. Any opportunity to move would be good for Anthony, "but most importantly we need to concentrate on his sensory integration," she stressed, enunciating the syllables like a kind of mantra. Sensory integration. Another theory.

Haley called Anthony over to a swing that looked like a hammock. He lay in it and she pulled the ropes, tightly binding him in like a baby swaddled in blankets. It felt good. He enjoyed the pressure because it reminded his body it had limbs. Too often he felt distant from his own body. His body noticed its boundaries with the tight pressure and he liked that, but sometimes his poor sensory regulation meant he got too much sensory input too quickly. Overwhelmed by the awareness of his body suddenly bounding intensely into his attention, Anthony urgently longed to escape his swing.

He would have loved to regulate his sensory input like a normal, to have normal body awareness, to be able to feel at all times where his body was in space. The tightness helped him with this sense of proprioception, or body awareness, but he had those horrible neural pathways, which instead of taking in the sensory input of the tight pressure gradually like a normal system would, quickly overflowed and the input became a sensory bombardment. Anthony panicked. He began to struggle, frantically trying to get out of the hammock that enveloped him tightly, like quicksand. Haley ran to try to center him. "It's okay," she told him. "Let me try to spin it to calm him."

Haley was guessing. She had no idea why Anthony was out of control so suddenly. He began to twirl, feeling helpless and trapped. In the hammock, his body finally began to regulate itself, gradually. He felt less bombarded by the pressure as his body acclimated. He made little squeals hoping to get out but Haley twirled him more. It was strange, his sensory system. One moment he was fine, the next he was overloaded so much he was panicked. Haley finally stopped the hammock. His head spinning, Anthony lay there unmoving for a few seconds trying to get stabilized.

Haley looked at him. "Let's go to the table," she said. It was time for fine motor work. She had an array of objects to work his baseball gloves into functioning hands. First, he had to put circles into circle holes, triangles into triangle holes, x-shaped blocks into x-shaped holes and squares into square-shaped holes. Anthony was bored and frustrated, and he wanted to go home. He jumped up from his seat and ran to the door. Haley got him by the arm. He scratched her. She let go. He ran away from her, back to the trampoline. She ran, too, but she wasn't there yet. So, Anthony jumped as hard as he could, higher and higher. "Come down, Anthony," Haley called. He tuned her out. The freedom to ignore was blissful. Was there a person on earth more micromanaged than Anthony? "Do this." "Do that." "Touch this." "Pat your head." "Look at me." "Find lemon." "Wipe your face." "Hands quiet." "Toys all done." "Touch your nose."

Ignoring was his personal peasant's revolt from the nobility telling him what to do all the time.

On the other hand, Haley was nice. Her intentions were

all noble and honorable. But like the others in Anthony's professional team, her understanding of him was limited. Haley's sessions had many fun activities. He liked the trampoline and many of the swings. He enjoyed the climbing obstacle courses she built. Yet all his treatments and therapies were filled with guesses. Many were wrong. Some helped. Haley cared and tried. But, like Nina and Natasha, her training was perhaps her biggest obstacle, because it made her *think* she knew what was going on inside a person who couldn't communicate. That was the gap. Being unable to communicate in any way meant the gap could not be bridged. So, Anthony had treatments, lots and lots of treatments, by guessers. Anthony had more fear that he might never be understood than confidence that he would. He jumped until Haley finally climbed onto the trampoline to pull him away.

11

Peter, Autistic Superstar

Peter was the same age as Anthony. He had the same diagnosis. He also worked with Natasha, Nina, Charlotte and Alyssa in the ABA program, and Anthony and Peter also shared the same speech therapist. In fact, Peter was her star pupil. Their lives were practically parallel, but in every professional comparison with Peter, Anthony came out looking bad. Peter learned his drills faster. He learned to follow instructions quickly. He spoke with clear articulation and he looked fairly normal. He occasionally had temper tantrums, but otherwise Peter was the dream student.

To Anthony, Peter seemed to be the luckiest autistic guy in the universe. On the journey they shared, Peter was nearing the finish line and Anthony was barely out of the gates. The ABA data showed Peter learning new words rapidly, so rapidly he was doing the most advanced drills out there. Dr. Hagerty loved to remind people that he helped make some autistic kids lose their diagnosis. They may have been born impaired, but hard work, dogged perseverance and a little luck made a boy like Peter succeed. A case like Peter was the reason Dr. Hagerty had his reputation. He had many such cases, proof of the efficacy of his methods. Peter was an autism success story.

A stubborn case like Anthony confounded Hagerty, and everyone else. After years of intensive ABA, Anthony had progressed in his drills, but in no way, was he looking even remotely close to normal. He had reached the point that many professionals believed to be virtually hopeless. They might help mitigate his symptoms but he would never "recover," in the jargon of the trade. So, Anthony knew he was an autistic failure. He could not prove his intelligence, like lucky Peter. He knew that, because Nina and Natasha and everyone else also worked with Peter, they could not help but compare the boys. Anthony prayed inside to be like Peter. If only he could make his body obey him he could perform perfectly on his discrete trials too. But instead he was one of those frustrating kids who made Natasha and his team carry on with false optimism.

Anthony's mom and Peter's mom were friends, so Peter came over occasionally. He was supposed to play with Anthony but he always played with four-year-old Gary. Even though Anthony and Peter were the same age and Gary was younger, Peter and Gary were more in sync. They played computer games, Legos and even imagination games, while Anthony retreated to his room. But sometimes Peter's short fuse interfered.

Saturday afternoons offered a brief respite from Anthony's rigorous training. They were good days for play dates and his mother always hoped that Peter's play skills would influence Anthony for the good. Peter played pretend games with plastic food, stirring and cooking elaborate pretend meals. Gary loved to join in. Anthony didn't play pretend with the plastic foods. He lined them up in rows. In ABA sessions, he followed pretend play scripts and was prompted to put a plastic chicken leg in a plastic oven and then bring the plastic chicken leg to his mouth or he was prompted to put a plastic cow in a plastic barn. It was a go-through-the-motions charade. It was very hard when he had to play with Peter. Their mothers always watched and mentally compared. Peter's happily. Anthony's sadly.

Gary compared too. "My brother doesn't talk. He doesn't

play," Gary said, hoping to coax Peter into explaining what he couldn't understand. Gary knew that Peter had been diagnosed with autism too. But Peter only wanted to focus on his game. He was scrambling pretend eggs.

"Your turn, Gary," he answered flatly. He wanted Gary to make eggs too.

"How come you talk and Anthony doesn't?" Gary persisted.

Your turn!" Peter replied loudly. He was getting annoyed with the conversation. Peter had trouble picking up the social cues that Gary wanted to talk about other things while they played. Things he couldn't answer. He was focused only on preparing his eggs.

"Okay!" Gary yelled. "I just wanted to know!" He took his turn angrily. "Here's your stupid eggs!" He tossed the eggs toward Peter.

"Don't yell! Don't throw the eggs!" Peter shouted. He had trouble turning off his angry switch once it was activated, once his routine was disrupted. Instead of calming down he escalated. He kicked at the toy oven and it tipped over. He threw the plastic eggs across the room.

Gary was both used to it and a bit scared. He ran out of the room yelling, "Mommy, Peter is doing it again!" But it was Peter's mom who came running in. She squeezed her son tightly. She gave him a vest filled with weights to wear to try to help him calm down. He was screaming now, howling at the top of his lungs. Anthony, in the other room, had to cover his sensitive ears. After a little while Peter stopped. He had released his rage and was tired. His face was muddy with tear streaks. His mother told him to apologize to Gary. "I am sorry, Gary. Do you want to play Legos?" he said, a bit mechanically.

"I want to watch TV," Gary mumbled." He was speaking quietly because Peter had unnerved him. Anthony's mom suggested that Peter play with Anthony instead. Peter's mom agreed. Their mom break was over now.

Anthony's mother fetched him from his room, tugging him by the arm. The moms sat the boys at the kitchen table. Anthony's mother had to motor him through the game when he played with Peter. This time it was *Chutes and Ladders*. Peter loved this game. Unfortunately, Anthony was less fond of it. In the first place, he had trouble with board games because they were covered in busy pictures that looked like a jumble to him. If he micro-focused on the board he missed the goal. If he took in everything, he missed the point. So, he felt like a toad on a stool, croaking and wanting to leave. On the other hand, playing was beneficial if he wanted to integrate like Peter. Peter carefully picked his game piece, a little blond boy, like himself. Anthony grabbed the first one in front of him. It was a little girl, unlike him. They began to play, Peter counting spaces out loud, noticing the spaces that landed on a ladder or a slide. He climbed up the huge ladder square, nearing the top of the board. He was winning. He happily proclaimed, "I am winning!" Anthony wished he could share Peter's enthusiasm for moving an icon around a board, but he found it totally boring. His mom held his hand in hers and moved his piece for him, carefully counting spaces out loud.

"Oh look! You got a ladder," she exclaimed. He moved his piece up the ladder with his mom's hand over his, guiding him. The two mothers tried hard to make Anthony enthusiastic.

"Yay!" They clapped and encouraged. Anthony felt a bit like he was being punished because this activity was hard for him on so many levels: visually, attentively, fine motor and hand/ eye coordination. It left him filled with jealousy toward Peter who could play the game so easily. Lucky autistic Peter who could talk, play, build things, go to regular school and even "pass" for a normal. His tantrums were nothing compared to Anthony's pervasive ineptitude.

He is so lucky, Anthony heard himself think. He knew his entire team of behaviorists measured the boys against one another and compared his failures to Peter's triumphs.

The game went on for ten miserable minutes but eventually Anthony found his escape. He accidentally knocked the pieces over, spoiling the board. Anthony was clumsy, and it was nearly impossible for him to move his game piece around correctly. In any case, it set Peter off again. Peter's mom scrambled to fix the board and placate him, but Anthony took his opportunity in the chaos. He began twirling around the room, vocalizing and staring out of the corner of his eye at the picture whirring by him on the wall. Transported out of purgatory, he was high now.

Game over.

12

Speech Therapy with Bonnie

Bonnie was loud and energetic. She had many toys and activities designed to entice kids to speak. But Anthony had realized lately that he would never speak, so speech therapy was not exactly his favorite pastime. He had begun seeing Bonnie right after he turned three, newly diagnosed, his parents full of hope and fear. She saw almost all the autistic little ones in Anthony's suburb, specializing in toddlers and small children, to help them learn to talk during their so-called, "window of opportunity" period. But Anthony was already old for Bonnie's caseload—and still not talking. He felt that his opportunity windows were shut, the curtains pulled and a board hammered over them. He knew that speech therapy had not helped him to speak. That much was obvious. He saw other kids who had learned to enunciate or to communicate their thoughts at a basic level, or even more. Why couldn't he?

Anthony lived in apraxia. It thwarted him, blocking his mouth's movements, making his tongue a useless muscle and cutting him off from communicating with others. But Bonnie had another theory. She told his mother that the reason Anthony might be unable to speak was lack of motivation. "I don't believe in apraxia," she explained during a frustrating session in her toy-strewn office. "Have you ever seen an apraxic adult? This is all about wanting it." Anthony *should* be speaking by now, Bonnie explained to his mom, but he just didn't seem to care. And since he no longer seemed motivated by her candy rewards and high-fives, she didn't know how to spur him forward. Her toys just distracted him. They had reached a learning plateau, she told Anthony's mother. She thought he might benefit from starting fresh with another therapist.

Anthony listened from the corner of the room, where he was putting a big green plastic caterpillar in his mouth. It was obvious to him that his mother was frightened at the news. He felt disheartened at failing yet again. Once again, his body had betrayed him—and let his mom down too. His mother had hoped he would be able to speak by now. As for Anthony, he prayed every night for the gift of speech, but nothing ever changed. He might as well have wished to wake up with another foot. His mouth was not his friend.

The disappointment Anthony felt was huge. Bonnie had the reputation of being the best, most experienced speech therapist in the agency, and yet even she couldn't help him. His parents felt lucky that she had even agreed to continue working with him as he grew older. She almost never saw kids older than five. Bonnie had loads of enthusiasm, frosted blond hair, shiny diamonds on her chubby fingers and the foghorn voice of a hockey fan. Her lessons could be heard anywhere in the grey, drab hallways of the speech therapy building as she hollered instructions, corrections and praise with a larger-than-life energy and ear-splitting volume that she believed was necessary to engage the autistic child and snap him out of his detachment.

Bonnie, barely glancing at Anthony who was stimming with the toy caterpillar in the corner, explained to his mother that this would be her final session with him. From now on, she said, Anthony would be working with Cindy, a new therapist fresh out of school. "She's lovely," Bonnie assured Anthony's mother. "So skilled." And that was it. She gave him a hug, a high-five and a lollipop to wind up the session.

Anthony had mixed emotions. On the one hand, he was finally done with Bonnie after years of wasted effort. He had lots of resentment toward her. Her opinion that apraxia was totally curable implied to him that she thought he was a failure. She had often talked about the many kids she had cured and she told Anthony he could be one of them, if he only wanted it enough. Listening to her stupid opinions poisoned his heart. He had so many fears that he would never speak and never find a way out of his prison.

The Bonnies, Nathashas, Dr. Hagertys and the rest of them made it worse. By misunderstanding him and underestimating his intellect so profoundly, they made him feel hopeless. Hopeless people are sad, but they are also angry. Anthony had run out of patience with Bonnie and her opinions. He picked up a handful of her marbles and tossed them, watching them scatter around her office. His heart sank when his mother began picking them up. He had intended to leave them for Bonnie.

13

Sub Day

Anthony was having a bad day at school. Mrs. Lester was out ill and the substitute teacher treated him and the other students as if they had no brains. This went beyond normal boredom. Anthony felt like a character in a long, tedious movie that was slowed down. In the front of the room, the substitute talked in overly-enunciated tones, teaching nothing, dragging out the weather drill interminably. Anthony tried to sit still, composed and quiet but he was fidgeting in his seat. Meanwhile, Lily was on "hands quiet" patrol.

"What weather today?" the substitute teacher sang out. It was hot outside. She called Anthony up to move the sun picture from its place on one felt board to the felt board that showed the day's weather. His motor system was restless. He longed to run outside. "What weather?" she repeated. Anthony got up from his chair, stumbled to the front of the room and grabbed the first weather picture he saw. It was a raincloud with drops falling from it. It wasn't a shining sun and he knew it. The sunny picture was to his far left. He would have needed to turn his head, scan, search and find. Anthony was bad at that. It was like a bad dream compulsion that made him follow through by retrieving the wrong card. Now the substitute would think Anthony was dumb, like Lily already did. He might as well get it over and done with.

"No, no," the substitute said. "It is hot. No rain." She added, "Find sun." Anthony was frozen in his spot. Lily got up.

"He doesn't understand," she told the teacher. "He's been doing this every morning since pre-K and he still messes up."

Anthony was humiliated. Lily was always telling people how stupid he was in front of him. It was mortifying. He began flapping his hands in frustration. "Hands quiet." Lily told him.

The teacher patiently said, "Okay. Hot today. Sun."

Well duh, Anthony thought. He knew why they thought he was dumb. Day after day he got trivial answers wrong. He thought that his behavior was the perfect fooling machine. Inside was an intelligent boy. Outside was a boy who needed to be guided through a simple weather drill. Now, hand over hand, Lily motored him through it and placed the correct picture on the felt board, the Velcro back sticking to it. "Good job," the teacher and Lily applauded. Anthony had the feeling his day would be a long one.

Math came next. Out came the 1+1, 2+6, 4+5 worksheets. Anthony could sense that the substitute teacher observed his pathetic limitations with pity. He was supposed to fill out the worksheets, but he couldn't write. Lily shouted the first workbook equation at him, gesturing and enunciating each sound carefully. "Four plus five," she instructed, holding up her fingers. He was drowning in shame.

Who makes these programs for me? he thought. *Who decides that my life needs dumb-dumb math forever?* Anthony was getting upset. His flubbing hand made him appear lost. He figured he knew math better than Lily. He calculated in his head while *she* still used her fingers. As Lily shouted loud instructions and "hands quiet," Anthony felt that he'd become a curious object of intrigue commanding the substitute teacher's attention. It wasn't just Anthony. All the students' inabilities to perform rudimentary tasks seemed to baffle the sub. For tips, she turned to Lily and the other aides.

Anthony heard Lily approach the teacher and explain: Anthony had limited language processing and was lost in his own world. She added that his cognition was limited. Anthony agreed that her second point was valid, sometimes, but not her first or third. To be fair to Lily, she must have truly believed what she said. If she didn't, talking this way about another person in front of him would be horribly cruel. Still, Anthony had revenge fantasies of telling the world about Lily's limitations while her big dumb mouth was taped shut.

His mood was getting worse by the minute. Recess didn't help. His desire to escape was strong. He watched the movement of a group of kids running on the playground until they visually blended together, their images swirling and streaking artistically. Flap flap flap. Then they noticed him. "Stop looking at me!" one boy shouted. His friend started imitating Anthony. Then three boys started flapping and laughing. Anthony flapped more. It was his way of yelling at them, but it only stigmatized him further. Lily was looking at her phone and the substitute was oblivious. Mrs. Lester would not have let this happen.

"Ha ha. He thinks he's a bird." The boys laughed. Anthony was crying on the inside. He would have loved to play with them, but he couldn't. Now he was their target.

Suddenly Mrs. Lester's aide walked up. She was angry. "Boys, you stop this right now!" They looked nervous. "Whose class are you in? What are your names?" They knew they were in trouble. Lily looked up.

"What's happening?" she asked.

"Maybe you should keep an eye on your student," Mrs. Lester's aide angrily told her. "He's been bullied by these boys here." Lily stupidly defended herself.

"Well, luckily he doesn't know what they're saying," she said.

"Really?' said Mrs. Lester's aide. "How do you know?" Lily shut up. If the classroom aide didn't understand that, well, she wasn't going to get into a battle with her.

When Anthony returned to class after recess he was worn-down. He had no hope at all that his day would improve. Lily was embarrassed that she had been reprimanded and she took it out on Anthony, nitpicking his behavior incessantly. The clock ticked backwards, time moved so slowly, and the lost and confused substitute made the day longer still. Finally, the school bus came to take Anthony home. On the bus, he stared at the patterns outside the window. He felt forlorn. The other kids paid him no attention, so the window was his only friend on the bus. He returned to Autismland in an instant, grateful for the respite. It had been a long day spent slogging through quicksand.

Anthony's mom greeted him when he got off the bus in front of his house and immediately he felt overwhelmed by a huge wave of sadness. Being home was a relief as well as a release. His emotions rushed out. Anthony began to cry. His mom looked at him in surprise. "What's wrong, honey? Are you sick?" She felt his forehead. No, it wasn't hot. Anthony was so frustrated.

I want to tell Mom about my horrible day, he thought. He was showing distress because he felt sad, but the Autism Guessing Game was about to begin.

"Does your tummy hurt? Hurt tummy?" his mom asked, pointing to his stomach. Anthony yelled and tugged at his hand. His mother noticed the movement and immediately asked, "Does your hand hurt?" She took his hand and looked closely. It was dirty but not injured in any way that she was able to see. He hated the guessing game. When he was sad people always assumed he was sick or injured. He was never thought to just be sad about something. His heart was breaking a little because he couldn't make his mom understand him. He wasn't just sticking out his lower lip as he'd learned in his expressive emotions drills. He was really crying, and still his mother thought his pain was physical, not emotional. He healed a little when she hugged and kissed him and snuggled him until he relaxed. She may have missed the cause of his distress, but she knew the cure.

14

ABA Outside

The ABA lesson that afternoon was tough. Anthony's mood was morose. He felt trapped by his symptoms and angry at life. He was not in the mood for baby talk and "high five" over and over. Alyssa, the sporty Barbie, was there. "Hi kiddo," she chirped enthusiastically. "Ready to work?"

No, I'm not! Anthony screamed in his head.

"Good, let's go," she went on as if he had responded in the affirmative. His silence led her to believe he agreed with her. Passively he followed. He was so easily led around.

"He had a bout of crying today," Anthony's mother told Alyssa.

"Oh no, poor kid. Did he hurt himself?" Alyssa bent over her fluorescent green running shoe and tied her lace.

"I have no idea. He just burst into tears when he got off the bus."

"Hmmm," Alyssa pondered. "Maybe he feels sick?"

"He seems okay," Anthony's mom answered. "He just seems sad, you know."

"Well he looks fine now," Alyssa declared, tickling Anthony's stomach. Anthony laughed because he was ticklish, but he felt no happiness. Alyssa liked to tell him how he felt. She dismissed his emotions because he couldn't show them well. Even when he could show them, everyone, including his own mom, misinterpreted them as physical discomfort. He was not in the mood for his flashcards. Self-stimulatory behaviors beckoned.

Anthony sat at the table and immediately found his fingers

to be fascinating. He waved them before his face, staring intently. It was the same pattern. Like a tennis volley, it was now Alyssa's turn. "No Anthony. Quiet hands." Anthony put his hands down and immediately began shaking his head back and forth in a rapid "no" shake, over and over until he began to get a buzz. He was intoxicated by the visual stim. It was his triumph over Alyssa. Catch me if you can. She tried.

"Anthony, stop." "Anthony, no." "No head shake." "All done." "Stop head shake." Her voice receded. He was enjoying his power. He laughed, this time out of pleasure. "Maybe we need to walk a little outside first," she suggested. "Let's try to give him a more naturalistic educational experience today." Gandhi had triumphed over England. Anthony felt good. Maybe he could become free too.

Outside was much better because there were no flashcards, no drills and no logbooks recording his mistakes. He walked happily. Alyssa called him. She held a leaf. "Look Anthony, leaf." She picked up a dry, brown leaf and a green fresh one. "Touch green," she commanded. He did. "High five, smart boy." She tickled his stomach. "Touch brown." On and on, the walk incorporated lessons like this.

Anthony was satisfied because he was not at the table. On the other hand, he knew the answers to much more than the color of green or brown leaves. He had watched a science show for kids with Mark. Though his body was restless, that didn't stop his mind from taking in the lesson. As Mark lay on the sofa, listening in relaxation, Anthony took in the show while pacing in perpetual motion.

Now he wished he could ask Alyssa, *Do you know why it's brown?* He longed to explain the lessons he had learned about chlorophyll and the life cycle of plants. It was interesting information and Anthony retained all of it. Lessons floated around in his head on a repeat loop. Because he had no one to talk to about the things he saw and overheard, he thought a lot about them on his own. Sticking close to Mark, a science buff who lived on a diet of documentaries, was Anthony's slow path forward. In this way, he learned about magma and volcanoes. He learned about the dinosaurs. He learned about animal behavior. Anthony loved learning. Most of the time he was bored, re-learning things he had known since he was a baby, stuck, trapped, tired and scared. But sometimes he had the opportunity to listen and learn, like anyone else.

"Touch flow-wer," Alyssa said. "Good job. Pink flow-wer. Flow-wer is pink. Look. Purple flow-wer. Yel-low flow-wer." It was boring, but at least Anthony looked at flowers, not flashcards.

15

What If

When Anthony arrived at David's home, chaos reigned. Anthony's mom knocked on the door. David rushed to open it, then dashed away. He was stark naked. "Put on your bathing suit!" his mom yelled, chasing him. Anthony could see David's ribs and his pointy shoulder blades.

David was Anthony's best friend from school. He lived with his mom and older brother, Jason. His father had left when David was just four. He couldn't take the toll of autism on his life. David's mother, Robin, tried hard but she was overwhelmed a lot. Their home was practically Spartan. David was a human wrecking ball. His mom had put away anything pretty or breakable. The carpets and furniture were torn by David experimenting on them. The tables were covered in marker lines. His mother admitted it: David pretty much ran the whole house.

David dashed madly. He was having fun. His mom finally grabbed him and he fell to the floor, refusing to dress. "He loves the sensation of water on his bare skin," Robin said. "I think the bathing suit must be tactilely aversive." He slipped his narrow wrist from her grasp, ran into the yard and jumped into the pool naked. Robin sighed. "Are you okay if he stays like that?" she asked Anthony's mom. Anthony's mother shrugged. It was obvious Robin was worn down.

David manipulated his mom all day long for videos or attention or corn chips. He used his ornery moods to get her to give in. His mother believed he had no understanding of consequences and it certainly looked that way. David broke things, ignored instructions and more or less ate, or, more often, refused to eat, as he pleased. But Anthony knew his friend was clever. He saw his manipulations for what they were—the consequence of an exhausted mom and a frustrated, strong-willed son.

Still, it was nice for Anthony to visit. Anthony often felt nervous visiting other homes, but he never did at David's. Some people minded if Anthony touched things or wandered around their home. They watched him closely, alarmed at his unpredictable movements, afraid he might break something, but at David's home whatever he touched was fine. He could wander anywhere in the house. David spent most of his free time watching the same videos again and again. He refused to watch anything else and would become enraged if he was told no. Since David's mom was worn down, she didn't say no often. His teenaged brother, Jason, avoided the whole scene. He had built a life outside the house, playing a lot of baseball and football. So, when Anthony came over, he felt he had free rein to do as he pleased. David's home definitely had its problems, but it was not judgmental or afraid of autism. Anthony felt comfortable there.

Anthony jumped into the pool. It was big and he and David never had much interaction in it so didn't matter much that David was suitless. Anthony stimmed on the pool toys on one side and David liked diving for rings at the bottom of the pool at the other end. Still, it was a playdate. Both boys were happy to be together.

The moms poured themselves tall mugs of coffee and sat at a small wrought-iron table in the shade, near the shallow end, where they could see both boys. Robin tied her long auburn hair into a twisted ponytail. When she took off her sunglasses her eyes looked tired and they had rings under them. Robin said that David was driving her crazy. He kept her up all night because he had so much trouble unwinding and falling asleep. "I need to do something to help him."

Robin took a swallow of her coffee. It was too hot, but she barely noticed. Her sleep deprivation was at the point she hardly felt her own body sometimes. She was planning to try a new treatment, she told Anthony's mom, one that would purify David's gut, and hopefully help him sleep and possibly even communicate better.

She glanced at her freckle-faced son diving for rings at the bottom of the pool. "He has been through so many treatments," she said, counting on her fingers as she listed them off: "ABA, floor time, sensory integration, play therapy, speech therapy, chelation, fungal treatment, music therapy, gluten free diet, mega-vitamins, auditory integration. I'm probably forgetting something. I even got him crazy glasses in vision therapy. They looked like Coke bottle bottoms. He crashed into things for two days before they disappeared." She sighed. "Who knows if this will help, but what other choice do I have? Well, I guess it's just money. You've got to keep trying."

Anthony's mom was Robin's main support system. True, she thought some of this stuff was hogwash, but some of it, she thought, was worth a gamble. She had tried a few of the unusual treatments on Anthony, without much success, and she was totally devoted to the reliable ones, the essentials that everyone did: speech therapy, occupational therapy, ABA and a few others. She and Robin were always hoping that the next one would be the treatment that could make a big difference. Anthony's mom constantly wrestled claims and testimonials with her own gut instincts. "Do you ever feel we're being taken for a ride?" she asked Robin. It was such a confusing minefield for parents. "I mean there's so many claims. I don't know how honest they all are and only ABA is scientific and even that isn't helping very much."

Anthony stopped jumping up and down in the water. He moved closer to the pool steps, rubbing his hand back and forth on a blue pool noodle. But he was listening closely, as he often did. He rolled his eyes in his mind. *Yeah, right,* he grumbled in his head. *The logbooks make it 'scientific.'*

"Well, I don't know what choice we have," Robin said again, her voice rising. "I want to give David a chance. I just don't know how much he takes in. I think he's smart. Lots of times he seems to understand. Then he does things like today." Her voice trailed off.

Anthony wanted to yell, *He was teasing you! Do you think he didn't know you wanted him to wear a bathing suit?*

"I guess it's hard to tell," she said. She put her sunglasses back on and lowered her voice. "Don't you wonder if Anthony understands?" Anthony was listening hard now. So was David, who had maneuvered himself closer to the shallow side of the pool.

"Yes," Anthony's mom said emphatically. "I often worry how I talk in front of him. I mean, if he understood our supervisions...how awful."

"I doubt they could understand language that complex." Robin sighed again.

"But what if they do?" Anthony's mom pressed on. "Maybe I need to be more careful what I say in front of Anthony. I mean, imagine if he understood and couldn't show it."

Robin looked sad. "That's not likely," she said softly.

They sat quietly for a while, watching the boys, each straining to imagine what was in her own son's mind. Then Anthony's mother remembered the *Little House* reading session. She told Robin about Anthony hiding under his blankets after hearing the story about Pa in the cave. Robin gasped, "That's amazing."

"I know," Anthony's mom said. "I've been thinking about it so much. I brought it up to Natasha and she thought it was just coincidence. She said it was a stim. I tried to describe how he looked and responded but Natasha felt it had to be a stim because Anthony hasn't got enough vocabulary mastered yet." Robin nodded. Made sense.

Anthony had practically been holding his breath. Now he felt crushed. It was amazing how often these "coincidences" occurred. It was as though he was on a desert island, waving wildly to a small plane passing overhead. And now it was a speck on the horizon. Would it ever come back?

"Well," Robin said, "I kind of hope David *doesn't* understand. I've said so many awful things in front of him, he'd probably hate me. I haven't been a perfect mom."

"Who has?" Anthony's mom replied, wishing now that she had a cocktail in her hand instead of coffee, "Still, I'd rather he understood. Sometimes it really feels like there's a soul in there crying to come out."

She and Robin were programmed, though. Programmed by Dr. Hagerty, by Natasha, by the scholarly books and theories that filled their lives. To Anthony, it felt almost like his mom turned into an automaton when she spouted Hagerty-speak. Now she droned on. "Dr. Hagerty says it's wishful thinking. He says that what Anthony shows on the outside is a reflection of his inside. He says that if Anthony understood more he would show it." She see-sawed back and forth, weighing her instincts and what she saw in her son from time to time against what she had been taught. She had her doubts, she told Robin. Sometimes Anthony really did seem to be trying to show her that he understood.

"Or maybe I'm in denial," she said, the see-saw dropping with a thud on the side of hopelessness. "The majority of the time he's in his own world."

Anthony's mind swirled with mixed emotions. On the one hand, he was sick of Dr. Hagerty and Natasha and their insights. They were so good at lowering his mother's expectations and making sure she didn't stray from their dogmatism. But on the other hand, his mother had doubts. Now, he could dare to hope that there was a crack emerging in the wall of theories she clung to. It wasn't much to hold on to. But it was something.

16

Grandma

On the way home Anthony and his mother stopped at his grandmother's small but tidy apartment to pick up Gary. Gary needed that one-on-one attention from his grandma. Anthony tended to suck up all his parents' energy with his incessant unpredictable activity and the need to engage him constantly to stop him from stimming. It was hard on Gary, who was younger than Anthony but was forced to be more independent. Gary was in paradise at Grandma's oasis of hugs, games and snacks. She wasn't burned out, worn out or overwhelmed the way his parents were. She had raised three kids but admitted that her three kids were easier than one Anthony. Her intuition told her that she should give the other boys a haven from Autismland. This she did with gusto.

"Hi Mom," Anthony's mom called when they arrived. She scooped up Gary and hugged him. "How's my guy?"

"Good. Look, Mommy," he said, pointing to a warm loaf, "Grandma and I made banana bread."

'Oh wow, it looks delicious." She beamed at him. Gary smiled proudly.

"Where's Mark?" Grandma asked.

"He's at Jack's house. He's sleeping over," Anthony's mom said. Grandma nodded. Grandma knew Jack. He and Mark had been best friends since they were in kindergarten. Unlike most of Gary's friends or Mark's other friends who came over, Jack was relaxed around Anthony and took no notice of his odd behavior. Because of that, many times, Anthony's mom had tried to get the boys to include Anthony in their games to give Anthony some practice socializing. But even for Mark, who was always kind, and Jack, who was tolerant, this was really a thankless task.

Anthony lacked all the necessary skills to truly join in. He had no facial expressions, no gestures, no speech. Since his gross motor skills were atrocious, ball play was out of the question. Board games were boring to Anthony and he had a short, impulsive attention span and fine motor problems managing the pieces, which usually ended up in his mouth. He became a kind of anchor weighing Mark down. It was impossible for them to play the way they wanted with Anthony in the room. So, Mark's solution was to play at Jack's house as often as he could. Anthony's mom was resigned to that. Her eldest son needed his own life.

"How are things here?" she asked.

"Good! Gary is such a good helper," Grandma said, making sure to praise her youngest grandson in front of him.

Anthony, meanwhile, made a direct dash for his grandmother's room. On her dresser sat a paperweight with scores of lines and dots swirling inside the glass. His favorite. He brought it up to his eye and stared at the patterns. He was immediately lost in Autismland. He had his escapes planned everywhere he went. Certain objects seemed purposefully designed to bring on pleasurable visual highs. This paperweight was definitely among them. How Anthony wished he could explain it to Grandma. It was nothing personal. He wanted a hug, but this was a sensory compulsion. The paperweight was obsessively calling to him. He had to go to it. There was no other way.

He heard his grandmother ask, "Where's Anthony?"

"He's gone after that paperweight again, I bet," his mom answered. "I just don't know how to stop these behaviors."

"Maybe he needs them," Grandma suggested tactfully. She was a smart woman.

"Oh Mom, we've gone over this so many times. If we let him stim he can never learn to behave appropriately. Natasha says he has to be engaged all the time before the window of opportunity closes."

Mom, it's closed, Anthony thought, paperweight next to his eye, *if the window was ever even there to begin with*. Grandma stepped into her bedroom. She looked at Anthony with love and gently removed the paperweight from his hand.

"Hey little man, would you like some banana bread?" she asked.

"Mom, does it have flour in it?" Anthony's mom yelled from the kitchen. "You know he's gluten free."

"Okay then," Grandma asked, "how about a banana?"

"I want banana bread," Gary shouted.

Grandma was full of affection for her grandchildren but she wasn't sure how to connect to Anthony. She hugged, kissed and tried to play with him but she never knew how to talk to him. Anthony's parents made a lot of rules for her. Keep it simple. Talk slowly. Insist on eye contact. Drop articles and use few words. It didn't come naturally to Grandma. She had to be constantly reminded to stop speaking normally with Anthony.

In his heart, Anthony knew Grandma was hurting because she didn't know how to engage her beloved grandson. Anthony was hurting because he couldn't stop autism long enough to be like the other grandkids even for a minute. His mom was hurting because she was treading water all the time. Dr. Hagerty and Natasha claimed to offer life preservers, but they must have been made of cement. They never helped Anthony float. Instead, they kept him under water, and his parents frantically busy.

In any case, Grandma never followed the rules if she could help it. She had a hunch that all the demands and prodding were driving Anthony crazy. She worried that he was miserable inside, though she never suspected that he was thinking complex thoughts. Her middle grandson danced on his toes and looked lost while staring at moving water. He didn't look like a deep thinker to her, but he did look tired of drills. Grandma wondered what the point of all these drills was after all these years. Were they expecting a magic day to come and make Anthony fine? Her heart told her to give the kid a break.

The struggle between parent and grandparent was obvious. Anthony's grandmother had intuition and experience raising normal kids. Her intuition told her that disability or no, Anthony was just a young boy.

His parents knew this, of course, but they were frightened for him. They had read all the books, consulted with the best and been educated about autism, so they had a mission. Each intervention they tried was in the hope that this time it might change his neural wiring and help him to improve. Each time, those hopes were dashed. Robin ran after every new claim and treatment, and Anthony's parents ran after every treatment that seemed scientific, hoping, praying that the claims would prove true for their boy. Each time left them poorer. Each new diet or purification of some biological system was supposed to help reduce his symptoms, but his autism always stayed the same. His parents tried, like Robin, to find the Holy Grail, but in the end, they were always left only with ABA and its "scientific" discrete trials. But even that door was starting to close. Anthony's mom often thought about what Dr. Hagerty said in one lecture she had attended. "By the age of eight, the path of an autistic child has been made clear."

Grandma didn't know the theories. She patiently tried to follow the rules of diet or interaction when she remembered, but she trusted her own knowledge of children to guide her more than textbooks and theories. She knew Anthony's parents were stressed and trying their best, and she tried to help by babysitting when she could. Beyond that, autism was a confusing world she had no special tools for, except her love.

17

Brothers

The ice-cream truck tinkled its tinny tune and the boys ran to find it. It was Sunday afternoon and Mark had agreed to play with Anthony at the playground for a bit while their mom sat on a bench watching. Their mom always asked Mark to give his brother some appropriate playground experience before running off to do his own thing. Today she asked Gary to help too. If his mother or father wasn't playing with him, Anthony usually ended up playing alone there, despite his craving for new friends. He might approach a kid engaged in play and stand nearby, hoping to be included. But Anthony didn't talk. He stared too long and too hard and the other kid would quickly become uncomfortable. Mark tried to help his brother, guiding him around the playground climbing structures and letting him shoot down the slides with him, foot over shoulders. If Mark took the initiative to include Anthony, other children usually joined. Kids looked up to him and followed his lead. Those were the best days.

Today, Gary had taken the lead. He ordered Anthony around in a loud voice. He liked to show how big he was bossing around an older child. "No, Anthony. Don't eat that." "Climb the ladder now, Anthony." A woman watching over her own children smiled admiringly at him for helping his brother. Gary felt important and Anthony felt ashamed. At home, Gary whined incessantly about Anthony bugging him. He complained that Anthony made noises while he tried to watch cartoons, or that he touched his toys. But in the park, Gary loved the attention. There, he was solicitous and attentive.

Anthony hated the expression on his little brother's face. Maybe he could get a flashcard with a picture of four-year-old Gary's self-satisfied expression to add to the other facial expressions he was constantly drilled on, the ones showing stereotypically happy, sad, mad and surprised facial expressions. "Touch irksome smugness." He was sure to recognize it. Anthony knew it wasn't easy for Gary either, having *him* for a brother, while also being in the shade of the glorious Mark. He hoped that Gary would soften over time.

The ice-cream truck came to a stop next to the park. As part of his autism treatments, Anthony was on both a gluten- and casein-free diet, which deprived him of both the dairy in ice cream and the wheat in cones. The only treats he could get from the ice cream truck were sugary popsicles full of dye. But his mother had recently determined that the sugar and food coloring made him hyperactive, so even *that* goody was taken from him. Still the truck's telltale tune was like Pavlov's bell. All three brothers took off towards it.

Mark and Gary were used to autism but it still embarrassed them. Anthony's physical compulsions and socially inappropriate behaviors humiliated them before strangers. Sometimes Anthony gazed intently at the patterns of the falling sand he poured through his fingers on the playground while yelling weird sounds, and all the other children stared. Even Mark tried to pretend he didn't know Anthony then. But what happened next was worse. Anthony dashed past Mark and Gary straight to a little girl holding an ice cream sandwich. Before even he knew what was happening, his hand was lunging for it.

"Hey," the girl yelled. "It's mine!" Mark bolted forward and strategically maneuvered himself to block Anthony, who began loudly vocalizing. Mark turned bright red. Gary wouldn't even look at him.

By this time, Anthony's mom had caught up. "I'm so sorry," she apologized to the little girl's annoyed mother. The woman looked at Anthony flapping his hands and yelling gibberish after being thwarted.

"Don't worry about it," she mumbled. "It's no problem." His autism never failed to make strangers feel guilty for their irritation.

For Anthony, it was just another reminder that even his brothers weren't really his friends. Mark tried to reach out at home. He invited Anthony to sit with him when he watched television. He told him jokes and stories. Mark never talked dumb to Anthony and Anthony loved those moments. They gave him hope. But at moments like these, or when Mark had his own friends over, it was a different story.

Pretty much all of Mark's and Gary's friends felt a lot of discomfort around Anthony, except for Jack. It was obvious though they sometimes tried to hide it. If Anthony was running around the house yelling nonsense noises and waving his arms, which was often, Gary's friends might stop and stare, perplexed and fascinated, while Mark's friends would rush straight to Mark's room and then retreat behind the closed door. These episodes filled Anthony with sorrow because he wanted so much to be in that room. He heard the laughter and he knew he was cut off from the fun. He didn't blame Mark because Mark had a right to his own friends. It was the realization that normalcy lay behind the door and Anthony was on the other side of it that hurt.

His mom and dad knew the sibling dynamics were complicated. They encouraged interacting but they didn't want to burden Gary or Mark with responsibility for their brother's happiness, so his parents tried to be Anthony's playmates and his best friends because there was no one else to fill the role. They played when others gave up or fled from Anthony. They persevered with the board games, Legos, trampoline, or any other activities they could tempt Anthony to join because they hoped it would help him. They could lure Gary and Mark in sometimes, but it was hard when things went awry and, after all, they were only kids. After the ice cream truck fiasco, their mom sensed that Mark and Gary needed a little time to play on their own. She took Anthony to the swings and gave his brothers a reprieve from autism.

18

Dad

Playing with his dad was the most fun part of Anthony's home life. His father joked and tickled and made Anthony feel almost normal when their play was physical, rather than the so-called skill building "play," like board game exercises and computer literacy programs, that Anthony tended to do with his mother. His dad preferred throwing a ball or riding a bike with Mark and Gary to board games or video games anyway. And intuitively, he knew that physical play was the way to connect to Anthony. If it wasn't swings, it was the hose, or the scooter, or the trampoline, or the tickle-monster. His dad could play actual sports with Mark or Gary, but with Anthony he could just jump and chase. It had to be good enough. And for Anthony, it was. He loved horse-play. He would laugh and laugh with his father.

It wasn't easy for Anthony's father to have three such different boys. He tried to be involved individually with each of them because they all needed attention. But Anthony mostly sapped his energy, draining his dad's already work-depleted supply with his relentless hyperactivity and stims. His father left for work early, battled a miserable commute and spent his day crunching numbers in front of a computer. He was tired. But he tried hard to juggle his life and be a good father to all his sons and a good husband to his wife. He loved having three active boys. But playing with all three together was tough.

"Come on Anthony, play with us!" his dad called. Anthony was sifting the sand at the park. He needed a lot of attention to keep him engaged. If his dad was tossing a ball to Mark,

Anthony stimmed. If his dad tossed the ball to Gary, Anthony stimmed. If Mark and Gary tossed the ball to each other, Anthony stimmed. If they tried to include him, he just stood in his spot, bored and indifferent.

Chasing games that ended in tickles worked best for Anthony. Once caught, Anthony would get tickled like crazy by dad, Mark and even Gary. It was a fun sensory rush and he felt part of the game. But when it was time for him to chase Gary, Anthony would freeze again. His dad would take him by the hand and tug him. He motored Anthony to tickle Gary, but Anthony didn't know how, so then his dad became a tickle monster, tickling all three boys.

It was nice to be included. It was hard on Anthony's parents because they wanted to give Anthony normal play experiences, but his motor and tracking challenges made the activity tedious for his brothers, and for Anthony. Anthony stayed until he could escape—to a swing, or a trampoline, the television or even his grandmother's paperweight. When he retreated to his escape, this allowed his dad the opportunity to do things like throw a ball normally with his other sons. Anthony's family tried hard to include him in their activities, but autism was a huge barrier between him and normal pleasures.

Today, though, his dad wanted to try to get Anthony to play ball. He wanted Anthony to play catch with his little brother.

"Please, Daddy," Gary protested. "Can't *we* just play?" Gary begged his dad to play with just him a little longer. They played ball and Anthony watched the sand fall, getting absorbed in the patterns. His dad was concerned he was getting too much in his head. It was hard to pull him back when that happened. His dad called Anthony again.

"Wait here, Gary." He walked over to Anthony and took

him by the hand. "Sand all done," he said. "Time to throw ball." Gary looked frustrated. Anthony ruined his games every time. His father handed Anthony the ball. "Throw ball to Gary," he commanded. Anthony tossed the ball sideways. It rolled down the slope to no one. He watched it roll, but didn't move to get it. "Gary, can you get the ball?" his dad yelled.

"I didn't throw it! Make Anthony!" Gary was defiant. Anthony had ruined his fun again.

"Okay, Gary, get it this time. Anthony will get it the next."

Gary marched off, angry. He picked up the ball and threw it sideways so it landed far from Anthony.

This was the way their sad routine inevitably played out. Father tried to include Anthony and motivate him to participate in a normal activity. He coaxed and encouraged him, working hard to stay upbeat. Gary sulked because his fun with his father felt over for him. Meanwhile, Anthony hated the ball because he was uncoordinated and his body wouldn't obey him. He lacked the ability to throw or track it with accuracy so he didn't even try. His father wanted the play to be fun for everyone, but Anthony was Gary's fun-killer. There was no way his dad could please everybody, but he simply could not let Anthony live a life sifting sand. To engage him required herculean efforts by his family, but this too made Anthony feel ashamed. He exhausted his parents and made his brothers resentful. Yet, Anthony needed these moments.

"Stop throwing it sideways!" Gary was getting furious.

Anthony threw sideways because he lacked the motor ability to throw correctly. Tossing the ball to the side was simple. He could do it without thinking. He didn't need to simultaneously look, aim, control his movements and pay attention.

Anthony's dad came to the rescue. He stood behind Anthony and motored him to throw forward. With his dad's help, Gary was able to play catch with his brother, but he hated it. The fast pace was gone, and also the laughing. On top of that, he was expected to encourage Anthony, who became the focal point of the activity. For his part, Anthony knew Gary didn't want him there, which made him less interested in throwing than ever. It was a vicious cycle and the family was stuck in it.

The break came when they went to the swings. Here Anthony and Gary were equals. Anthony did not have the ability to pump his legs in a coordinated fashion. He needed to be pushed and Gary liked being pushed too. Both boys enjoyed it when their father made them fly. On the swings, Anthony felt free. He was soaring. His body wasn't holding him back. Visually, Anthony was intoxicated. The patterns and shapes around him blurred into streams of color. He never wanted to get off.

"Anthony, it's time to go," his father eventually said. Anthony clutched the chain on the swing tighter. No way he was leaving this heaven. "All done swing. All done, okay?" his dad repeated. Gary kept swinging. If Anthony wasn't budging, why should he? "Gary, get off now!" his dad yelled. "All done, Anthony. Off swing. Off."

"It's not fair. Anthony is still swinging," Gary cried, his sense of justice kicking in.

"Gary, I need you to show Anthony how to behave. He doesn't understand how to act. You be a good brother and show him it's time to get off." This tactic worked well. Gary loved being more capable than his older brother.

"Look Daddy, I'm off." He turned to Anthony and said, "Get off, it's time to go. Stop swinging. I want to go." Anthony complained in his way, making noises. His father caught him and lifted him off the swing. Anthony tried to speak.

"More," he attempted to pronounce. He grabbed onto the

chain trying to communicate his wish to stay.

Did he say "more?" That would have to be immediately reinforced. "Good job talking, Anthony," his dad said begrudgingly, wanting to leave but happy his son had actually used a word to communicate. He allowed a few more minutes on the swing as reward. But now the challenge of getting off began anew. After five more minutes, he was eager to get home.

"All done, no more swing." His father finally said. He was getting tired of the headache. Leaving the swings in the park was nearly impossible. If he didn't end it, Anthony would probably swing all night long. Anthony clung to the chain, now lying across the swing seat on his stomach, enjoying the pressure, moving himself that way. "No, Anthony. All done. Let go." Then in plain English his father muttered, "Can't you ever just listen and cooperate? Why does everything have to be a struggle?"

At least he's talking to me like a regular person, Anthony thought.

"I listen, Daddy, right?" Gary chimed in helpfully.

"Great, Gary. Okay Anthony, let go!" Anthony's father tried to pry his son's hands loose from the swing chain. He was sweating and swearing under his breath. "Fine, Gary, go swing five more minutes."

Gary had planned on this. So, had Anthony. They had managed to coax an extra ten minutes from their dad who knew how to enforce rules for Gary and Mark but was never sure how to insist for Anthony. Firstly, he never knew if Anthony understood his instructions. Secondly, he had pity for his son. Thirdly, he felt he always had to reinforce with a reward any attempt at speech. He knew that swinging was one of the few appropriate activities Anthony truly loved, but he also knew that rigidity and difficulty making transitions were symptoms he had to help Anthony overcome. He always felt torn. He loved his sons and tried to do the best he could, but he was horribly tired. He told his wife that he had the feeling that he was the modern Sisyphus pushing a gigantic boulder up the hill only to have it roll down again.

19

Turning Eight

It was Anthony's birthday. He was turning eight. Normally birthdays are joyful days and Anthony always enjoyed his party, but he also tortured himself with his annual birthday failure inventory. *I'm eight and I still can't tie my shoes. I still can't throw a ball properly. I still can't talk. I can't… I can't… I can't.* He could add thousands of 'can'ts' to his list. It made him mope and mourn. His greatest dream was to be able to talk. That would be the best birthday present imaginable. But time ticked by and Anthony was still not able to communicate his thoughts. So, although his birthday party was fun, he didn't feel thrilled like Gary did becoming a big boy or like Mark, who was getting ready to attend middle school next school year.

His party was at its usual location, a kid's gym. The guest list included his fellow flappers, stimmers and oddballs. David, of course, and other classmates were invited, and Peter, who went to a different school for high-functioning children. Mark's friend, Jack, and Gary's friend, Joey, were also there to keep the brothers happy too. The facility was mostly used as a pre-school gym and for toddler mommy and me classes, but they had known Anthony's family for years since all the boys had gone there when they were toddlers, and the gym staff had gained familiarity with autism. Still, Anthony was starting to outgrow some of the gear. This might be his last party here.

The gym's equipment had been arranged into an obstacle course. Kids had to climb over, through, around and under padded tunnels, bridges, ladders and bounce across a trampoline. The fun sensory experience made it enjoyable for all the kids with autism, as well as all the normal ones without it. Mark and Jack tore through the course like speed racers. They outpaced the clumsy, motor-impaired kids by far. Eventually Anthony's mother ordered them off the equipment for a while to give the slower kids a chance to make their clumsy way around but they finally compromised by making detours around them. Everyone had loads of fun. Anthony climbed up, bounced down, crawled through and maneuvered around the course. It was something he could accomplish and he had no self-consciousness in that setting. He just enjoyed himself.

Of all the kids diagnosed with autism at Anthony's party, Peter seemed to have the most going for him; his speech, his motor control, his play skills all set him apart from Anthony and his classmates since they had "low functioning autism," so called, while Peter had "high functioning autism," so called. Peter still had his challenges though. His threshold for frustration was low and his reaction to frustration was high, but this was improving. His recovery time from these outbursts had been shortening and their intensity was largely reducing. Hopefully soon these outbursts would disappear altogether. Then, Anthony figured, Peter's mom could write one of those books, "I cured my son's autism! You can too!" that people like Anthony's mom and Robin would buy and then wonder why they didn't have the same good fortune.

The children maneuvering around the course came to a sudden standstill. Peter was jumping up and down on the trampoline in the middle of the obstacle course. He wouldn't budge and the line of kids had built up behind him. The gym director went to him. "Jump across! Jump, jump, jump!" Peter continued to bounce up and down where he was. "No, I want to stay," he replied stubbornly. The director tried to take Peter by the hand to help him jump across the trampoline. "I want to jump!" he screamed, refusing to move. His mom looked up and sprinted to him. She could anticipate the meltdown that was emerging. Peter's father trotted over too. They whisked him off the trampoline to his furious shrieks. The line of kids then began to move their way through, under the supervision of the gym staff and their parents, while Peter's parents retreated to a far corner where they held him until he calmed down. His rage pierced the room for a few minutes. Several of the kids held their hands over their ears due to their extreme sound sensitivity. And then, as quickly as it started, it was over. Peter returned to the obstacle course line, his parents now making sure he remembered to jump across the trampoline. And from then on, Peter was fine.

Soon, Bridget, the director of the gym, called all the children to gather for food. Almost everybody preferred to play rather than eat, but she herded them off the gym floor. Anthony loved his party and ran to the table with a big smile on his face. He enjoyed eating chips and hot dogs (on gluten free buns), and he looked forward to his gluten free cake. Half of the autistic kids there were on that hopeful diet and there was no bakery where they could find a decorated birthday cake from the autism diet regimen. Anthony got used to it, eating rice bread, rice noodles, rice cakes, rice cookies and rice ice cream. He accepted that the yummy, bready and dairy treats that his brothers devoured with enthusiasm were forbidden to him because of a theory about a brain allergy causing autism. Theory upon theory dictated Anthony's daily life, including his diet. The only gluten and casein he got were pilfered.

"Sorry, it's home made," Anthony's mother apologized for her amateur looking cake. It had nine candles, one for good luck. The parents and the normals sang Happy Birthday. Peter joined in too. The nonverbal kids sat and listened and helped Anthony blow out his candles. Once his food was finished, Anthony leapt up and ran back to the trampoline. He jumped and jumped because everyone else was still eating lopsided gluten-free cake. Now Gary and Mark came to join him. "Say cheese!" his mother yelled. Gary smiled and Mark smiled and Anthony showed his teeth. He tried to smile but had trouble showing happy on demand. Every posed family picture had radiant smiles on Gary and Mark and a ridiculous teeth-baring expression on Anthony. It wasn't a snarl. It wasn't a smile. It was more of an attempt that didn't lift his cheeks up, so it didn't look happy, just silly. "That's Anthony's camera face," his parents explained. He felt so embarrassed. Could autism leave him alone if only long enough to take a nice picture? The only way they could catch a smile was in a candid photo. His face could smile, just never on purpose. Still, it was a happy day. Anthony felt like a regular kid most of the time.

20

Goulash (again!)

Anthony was finally off his gluten- and casein-free diet. His mom was no longer sure that all those years of trouble and expense had been worth it, or even made much of a difference behaviorally. She and the behavioral team had monitored him closely to see if the dietary change had affected his attention, mood and skills. The jury was still out. Now, six months after his eighth birthday, Anthony was dying to savor the forbidden fruits he had been denied for so long.

They were at what had become his family's favorite restaurant, near his grandma's home. It had a huge menu with lots of selections for kids. It was dimly lit, bustling with people and friendly staff, a place perfectly suited to a boy like Anthony, where he could make noises and flap his hands, and no one noticed. There were comfy booths with high backboards, so Anthony couldn't climb into the next booth and disturb the diners. They always sat in a booth by the window.

There were maybe a hundred dishes on the menu, but Anthony's menu consisted of just one item. Two years ago, his grandma had been eating goulash and potatoes there and it looked delicious. His hand shot out and grabbed for her plate. He pulled her goulash in front of him and disdainfully shoved away his boring burger patty (with no bun). The gluten-free chips his mother always carried for him everywhere sat in a plastic baggie at the side of his plate. He didn't want to give his grandmother her dinner back. Everyone laughed.

"Wow, he is really enjoying that dish," his mom observed, surprised and delighted at the discovery of a gluten/casein free meal he liked. From that day on, everybody thought Anthony only wanted beef goulash.

The meals were big and Anthony was starving. They had just come back from a long walk on the pier. Sea air made him particularly hungry. The perky middle-aged waitress handed out menus. "Hi, hons," she said to Anthony and Gary. "We've got chicken nuggets, fish sticks, macaroni and cheese, spaghetti and meatballs and pizza on the kids' menu." Mark had aged out of being a 'kid' there.

Anthony hungered for pizza, and he was at long last allowed to eat it, but when his mother asked him if he wanted goulash for dinner, his mouth, on neurological auto-pilot, said, "Yes." His mouth always said yes. Why did they even bother asking him?

He flapped his hands in frustration. It was an *I'm sick of goulash and I really want pizza and my mouth just said yes to goulash* frustration. It was trapped frustration. The waitress came back to take their order. She went around the table writing down what people wanted. When it was Anthony's turn, his mother spoke up. "Goulash for him."

"One goulash for the young man," the waitress said. He flapped his hands.

When she returned with the food, Gary got what he wanted. It was lucky for him that he could talk. He got his spaghetti and meatballs with garlic bread. The garlic bread looked good. Mark got what he wanted, too. He got a hamburger with fries he loaded with ketchup. Mom and Dad got what they wanted, of course, and Grandma got what she wanted. Anthony looked at his plate. He had the wrong dinner in front of him. He didn't want it. It was revolting. His stupid mouth. As always, his brain was screaming no and his mouth said yes anyway.

The goulash might have been delicious but it was bitter to Anthony. He pushed his dish away. "Is he developing food aversions?" his mom asked.

"Maybe he wanted something else," his grandma suggested.

"But he always loves beef goulash," his mom insisted. "And he said yes when I asked him. Maybe he's sick?" she touched his forehead. Anthony had no patience for this.

I want pizza, he thought. He flapped his hands harder. Gary's garlic bread looked tasty.

"That's mine," Gary yelled when he noticed Anthony's hand moving toward his plate. Anthony was frustrated. He was starving and he had nothing but unwanted stew. Grandma's salad did not look appealing, nor did mom's salmon nor dad's hamburger. The only foods that called his name were Gary's garlic bread and Mark's French-fries. His dad didn't even have fries. He had potato salad. Anthony tried to sneak fries off his brother's plate.

"Mark, can you give him some?" his father asked. Mark reluctantly handed Anthony some of his precious fries. Everyone had gone tense, worried that Anthony might act up in public. They didn't want to get him another dinner. On the other hand, Anthony clearly was not going to eat his. His mom ordered him a large side of fries and made a collection of food "donated" from everyone's plate; a meatball from Gary, salmon and rice from Mom, some of Dad's burger and some of Grandma's salad. The only things Anthony touched were his fries and the bun from his dad's burger.

"It's awful. He's addicted to gluten," his mom fretted. "He won't eat anything but starch. Maybe we need to get him back on the diet."

Have you looked at Gary's plate? Anthony thought. *Spaghetti and garlic bread. And he gave me his meatball because he didn't want it!* Anthony's mom interpreted everything he did by referencing a theory or symptom. It was frustrating to be so stuck that a simple meal was a reminder that he had no means to communicate his desires.

The family ate and Anthony enjoyed his gluten-free fries and his father's glutinous burger bun. He never had enough fries to suit him. The pile of fries in front of him averted a crisis and the tension subsided. Anthony's family tried so hard to be an ordinary family, but autism was on everyone's mind, all the time. They took the goulash home in a takeout box.

21

Getting Harvey

The day Harvey came to live with Anthony's family brought many different reactions. Gary was thrilled, Mark in heaven, dad upbeat, mom wary and concerned, and Anthony, in full phobic flight mode.

Like so many of his friends, Anthony was terrified of dogs. They moved unpredictably. Their barks pierced his brain like a loud spear. He had to cover his ears whenever he heard them. The only dog in his life belonged to his grandma. He was not a big dog. He was not an active or a noisy dog. But he moved, and that was sufficient to terrify Anthony. His grandma tried to get him used to Charlie and it sort of worked. Over time, Anthony had learned to touch his back with two fingers and to enter her home without feeling afraid.

Gary and Mark wanted a dog desperately. They begged and begged their parents. Mark promised to feed it and take care of it. But his mom was firm. Anthony was scared and a dog was too much work. His dad was on Mark's side. He believed that the only way to help Anthony overcome his dog phobia was to live with a nice friendly dog.

"He won't even set foot in the front door if we get one," his mom fretted.

"That will be short-lived," his dad replied. "He'll adjust quickly."

"But look at Charlie," his mom offered. "That took forever."

"He isn't our dog. He doesn't live with us," he said. "I think Anthony will love it. It will be good for him and I think Mark and Gary could use a pal too."

His mom finally gave in. "I'll consider it," she said, "but not a dog that's more than ten pounds."

Anthony's dad had other ideas, but he knew initially to keep them to himself. He had noticed that the high-pitched yap of a small dog hurt Anthony's ears more than the deep woof of a larger breed. He did his own investigating, trying to find a breed that had therapeutic sensitivity. No matter the breed or size, from Anthony's point-of-view, any dog was a vicious, drooling, kid-eating monster, especially fond of eating nonspeaking autistic kids.

The dog his father ultimately selected, Harvey, was a German Shepherd. He was seventy pounds bigger than the ten-pound limit his mom had originally decreed.

Anthony's dad had contacted a German Shepherd rescue group and explained the situation. He had three young boys, one of them autistic and scared of dogs. He needed a dog that could help his son get over that. The rescue lady immediately told him about Harvey. He was eight years old—same as Anthony—and his owner had recently died. He was calm and sensitive and used to living quietly.

"That's how he came to us," she explained on the phone. "He's still a healthy, active dog and he has a lot of life in him. Another plus is that he already knows his commands and is housebroken."

Gary, Mark and Anthony's dad drove out together to the rescue place, and Gary and Mark loved the dog from the beginning. He looked forlorn and confused but he stood calmly and wagged his tail slowly. Gary threw a ball for him and Harvey chased it. That settled it for Gary. Harvey was in. Mark patted him on the head and hugged him and Harvey leaned in and licked Mark on the nose. That settled it for Mark. They took him for a walk. He didn't pull. He remained mellow even when surrounded by the loud barking symphony of the other dogs who were waiting in their cages to be adopted. "He's a great dog. He's just a little old," the boys' father said.

"He's perfect" the boys replied in unison.

The ride home was one of pure joy for Mark and Gary. They couldn't believe they had actually gotten a dog and a great big one at that. It was rare for their wishes to supersede their brother's fears. Both boys petted Harvey and talked to him the whole way home. When they pulled into the driveway, their mom stepped out. "Oh my God, you have got to be kidding me," she said, shaking her head. "He's huge. What were you thinking?"

"He's the best, Mommy," Gary yelled.

"He's very good, honey," Anthony's dad told her softly. "Very calm."

"Okay," she said skeptically. "But if Anthony won't go in the house, the dog goes out."

"I'm sure we'll work it through." His dad held Harvey loosely by his leash. He was using his soothing, confident tone, the one that made mom and the boys trust him. "Let me handle it, please." His dad called to Mark, "Mark, can you please go get Anthony? Tell him we're going for a walk. I'll be at the corner with Harvey."

Mark ran in, excited. Gary hopped up and down in anticipation. Dad turned to his wife, "Let's all try to be super calm. No jumps or remarks if Anthony screams. Our calmness will help keep Anthony unafraid." She looked doubtful but said she would try. She liked dogs too.

Mark came out holding Anthony by the hand. They walked down the block together. Gary skipped nearby. Anthony saw the dog and immediately became anxious. "Keep walking but stay two houses behind us," his dad said over his shoulder.

"Okay, Dad," Mark yelled. Their mom took Anthony by the hand and Mark moved to be nearer to the dog.

"We're walking to the park," his dad announced, "to swing."

Anthony was conflicted. He loved the swing but feared the dog. But the dog ignored him and was far enough away. Mark asked if he could walk Harvey. He proudly held the leash, looking down at the dog with joy. Gary begged to walk Harvey next. He strutted like a little king. Harvey behaved like a calm gentleman. In the park, Anthony was wary, but his dad pushed him on the swing while his mom and brothers gushed over Harvey, hugging and stroking him. "I love him," Gary declared. "He's the best dog ever." Anthony refused to go near him.

On the way home Anthony walked with his father while his mom held Harvey's leash. Whenever Harvey turned his head Anthony yelled and ran back. But his father gradually moved closer and closer to Harvey, and before Anthony knew it he was ten feet away from the beast, then five. Anthony had to fight the panic, but the dog ignored him. Harvey had no interest in eating Anthony that he could see, and his dad was sneaky. They were right next to the dog now. They walked without incident, except when Harvey turned his head. Then, Anthony would jump back. They circled the block, two, three, four times. By the time they finally got home, the dog walked right into the house with them, and Anthony didn't even object. Harvey lay down on his dog bed and fell asleep.

Anthony watched cartoons on TV. He kept looked over at Harvey, but since the dog remained sound asleep Anthony's fear diminished. His mom then urged him to walk right up to Harvey and touch his back with one finger. Harvey raised his head and wagged his tail. That was movement. Terrifying!

Anthony's mind raced with fears. The dog had moving parts —long legs, big teeth, a loud bark. He was unpredictable and now he lived in their house. It was like living with a wild grizzly bear, Anthony thought. But he was already warming up to the idea.

It shocked everyone but after two days Anthony was used to living with his grizzly bear and Harvey showed a remarkable kind of sensitivity to Anthony. He seemed to sense that something about the boy was different and he was very calm near him. He let Anthony pet him, not too soothingly, with patience. In contrast, when he played with Mark and Gary he ran and roughhoused. After two months, the whole family, including Anthony, wondered how they had ever lived without him. Harvey was the best therapist Anthony ever had.

22

So Skilled Cindy

Eight months had passed since Bonnie, Anthony's longtime speech therapist, had announced that he needed a change. That change turned out to be "so skilled" Cindy. She was middle-aged with a close-cropped haircut that emphasized her giant earrings which swayed like a hypnotist's amulet every time she moved her head. Her features were angular and hard, the opposite of plump, soft Bonnie's. While Bonnie was loud and energetic, trying to wake autistic kids out of what she saw as an inattentive stupor, Cindy was her inverse. She was phlegmatic and soft-spoken. She *put* Anthony into a stupor. His time with Bonnie had stopped being productive a long time ago. His time with Cindy was worse. The only bright points were the lollipops.

In her sessions, if Anthony got an answer right she popped a lollipop into his mouth, then pulled it out immediately. Anthony soon realized that she left it there just long enough to enable him to tighten his teeth around it. He'd clamp down so hard that Cindy had to tug to try to get her lollipop back. But Anthony was often able to outsmart Cindy and pull the candy off the stick. This always annoyed her.

He felt mad at Bonnie. Her assurances that Cindy was competent seemed like little more than an attempt to get Anthony's mom to stop asking questions. Or maybe it had made her feel less guilty for closing an old case. He wondered if she believed what she told them. Regardless, Cindy not a big hit. But she was an innovator. She had made a great discovery in the field of autism: the power of lollipops to overcome apraxia. He really wished that Harvey could have been his speech therapist.

Cindy was about twenty years older than most of the speech therapists in the agency, except Bonnie, but she had only recently finished her training. Anthony was one of her first clients and he was immediately aware of her lack of experience. The lessons were tedious and the energy low. She was a speech therapist with a monotone. Anthony felt that he was biding his time so he made up his mind to entertain himself by getting all the lollipops he could from her. That would be his only goal. If she put a lollipop into his mouth, he would not let her take it out. He enjoyed antagonizing her with this game.

It was a Thursday in November when she stepped up her response. The windowless room, walls covered with speech therapy posters, seemed to close in around him. Most of Anthony's days blended together in a blur of monotony. But this day would stay with him. It would be like a stain in his mind he could never fully wash off.

"Let go, Anthony," she snapped, her monotone suddenly sharp as a razor. "Open your mouth." Cindy opened her mouth wide to make him understand. He bit off the lollipop candy. It was orange. "No, don't bite!" She looked irritated holding the second lollipop stick of the session in her hand. He quickly gobbled up the candy, chewing into the hard sugar and letting the sweetness float into him. Cindy looked confused and fed-up.

She held up some flashcards from a large stack on the table. "Touch house." He touched the house. "Touch elephant." He touched the elephant. "Touch pencil." "Touch door." "Touch money." "No, that's wrong." "Touch watermelon." On and on she droned, taking card after card, Siri-like, bland. Why did he even come here? Cindy did nothing exceptional in her lessons and certainly nothing more than Alyssa, Charlotte and Nina already did with him at home, and they were much nicer and a lot more energetic. Anthony persevered while his mom remained out of the room. This was a change from the Bonnie days. Cindy did not like parental intrusion.

Soon, she switched her lesson from comprehension drills to verbal output. "Mo-ney."

He imitated her, "muh-neh."

"E-le-phant," she droned. He tried to repeat it. He sputtered and made sounds, but it didn't sound like 'elephant.'

Cindy modeled, "Eh-eh-eh-eh. Le-le-le."

"Eh-eh." Hopelessly, Anthony tried to mimic her, but making the 'L' sound really was beyond him. She persisted, showing him her perfect tongue position. He tried to copy her, but the word was impossible to articulate. He wondered why Cindy didn't realize that. Her choice of vocabulary words always struck him as original. How often would he need to pronounce 'elephant?'

Anthony dreaded his speech lessons. What was the point? His mouth didn't listen to his brain. His tongue's only use in his lessons was for tasting candy. Cindy couldn't connect to him emotionally and her teaching technique was dreary. Week after pointless week he plodded on, knowing that she couldn't help him, that this was an exercise in futility. Sorrow made him give up trying.

"Elephant," Cindy persisted, pushing out each syllable again with apparent boredom. Anthony's response finally was to laugh, a humorless escapist stim that made work impossible. He giggled and giggled and couldn't stop himself. It fed itself. Cindy persevered in trying to engage him. "Elephant. Le-le-le." He laughed some more, delighted that she could do nothing. She couldn't pull him back and it was annoying and frustrating to her. Anthony knew how ridiculous his situation was. People go to speech therapy to learn to communicate and to get clear articulation, but year after year his progress was meager. He needed so many steps of incremental progression before he would ever be able to pronounce the word that Cindy was fixated on, let alone to communicate even basic thoughts verbally when his mouth didn't obey his mind. And there were so many other words more relevant to his daily communication needs than 'elephant' anyway.

Cindy snapped at him in irritation. "Don't you care if you talk or not?" Anthony laughed mirthlessly and shook his head in a rapid disconnected visual stim. He tuned her out, imagining how perplexed people would be if he tried to use her lesson in ordinary communication. *"Hi Anthony, what's up?" "Elephant," "What do you want to do?" "Elephant."* Or rather, "eh-nuh-fuh." He already had a ridiculously limited, unclear expressive verbal repertoire.

"You know," she grumbled, "I don't need to waste my time on this nonsense." He heard her frustration and relished it. He felt like he was on top.

Suddenly she grabbed his chin angrily, stopping his head from shaking. "Look at me," she commanded. "I work hard. You need to talk. You are lazy. You don't work. All you do is stim. You will *never* talk." Her ugly expression made Anthony feel sick. It occurred to him that being alone with her left him vulnerable. His mother sat in the waiting room, utterly unaware of what was going on. He felt frightened and defenseless.

Cindy held his chin. He couldn't turn away. "You think this is like a game? A big joke? *None* of my other clients act like this." Her hand hardened. She spoke to him normally. She was speaking to herself. She didn't think he understood her words.

Let go! Anthony screamed in his head. His mouth remained frozen silent. He looked up at the ceiling. It was off-white, with fluorescent light panels. He had to stop himself from seeing her angry face.

"I'm working, doing everything I can, and you waste my time and you just don't try. Every session! Week after week. Elephant! Le-le le." Her enormous earrings swished as she tossed her head.

"Nuh-nuh," he finally croaked.

After an eternity, her hand loosened. She seemed to relax somewhat. Anthony jumped up, flapping his hands wildly, and moved toward the door. Thankfully the session time had run out. When Cindy opened the door, Anthony ran toward his mother in the waiting room. He was vocalizing and flapping in excitement and distress. His mother looked up in surprise.

"How did it go?" she asked.

Cindy, poised and professional, replied, "Oh fine. His articulation is improving but he still struggles with those labio-dentals and especially the liquid 'L' sound. But we're working on it. Also, he seems to struggle with motivation." She relied on the fact that Anthony couldn't tell his mom what happened. He was climbing on his mother. "How do you motivate him to work at home?" Cindy asked casually.

"That's the eternal question," his mom answered with a strained smile.

"Well, I think Anthony and I are good friends," she said. "I'm just trying to find that golden ticket to get him to recognize how important these sessions are." She went up to Anthony and rumpled his hair. "See you next week." She took his hand and gave it a two-handed handshake, all smiles. Anthony hated her with his whole heart. He longed to go back to loud Bonnie or to anyone else in that clinic.

He walked to the car with his mother and sat in the back seat. She buckled him in. Suddenly the feelings overflowed and he began hitting his head hard. He had never hit himself before. His mother was shocked. Her face flushed with fear. "No, Anthony, stop! No hit." She took his hand and stroked it. He started to thrash wildly. "No Anthony, shhh." She turned on his favorite music and handed him a sensory ball. He threw the ball away and moved agitatedly in his car seat, hitting his head and tugging at his clothes. After what seemed a long time, he started to calm down. Shaken, his mom was finally able to start the car. She was crying when she called her husband on her cellphone.

"I'm leaving speech and Anthony just had a huge fit," she said between small sobs. "He was hitting himself. He's never been self-injurious before." Her husband's voice came out though the speaker.

"He hit himself? How?"

"On his head. Really hard. He was pummeling himself."

"Oh my God. Is he okay?" His dad sounded alarmed.

"He's calm now but he was totally wild. I hope this doesn't become a new behavior." David was self-injurious sometimes, she told him, "and it's horrendous. Robin sometimes has to keep him in tight, long sleeves so he doesn't scratch himself bloody. And I know another kid who has to wear a helmet because he bangs his head so hard. I'm scared," she said, panic rising in her voice. "I can't deal with that."

"Take a deep breath," Anthony's dad said, in his calming way. "He's fine now. He's never hit his head before, so let's not jump to conclusions. Maybe it's a one-time thing." He was quiet for a moment. Wondering. "Did something happen in speech to set him off?" he asked.

"I don't know." Anthony's mom came to a stop at a red light. She was searching for an answer. "Cindy doesn't like me to be in the room," she told him. "She feels he's old enough to be on his own and that my presence interferes with rapport development."

"That's odd, isn't it?" her husband noted.

"Lots of them do it. The rooms are so small. I didn't feel suspicious before today. She seems so professional and when they came out she was totally calm. But he wasn't."

"How was he?"

Anthony's mom recounted the scene, how Anthony had been crawling on her, flapping feverishly.

"That's not unusual," his dad said. It stung Anthony, even though it was true.

"No, but he seemed distressed," his mom replied. "I'm going to insist I be in the room next time. I have a bad feeling about this."

"Do you think she abused him?"

"I would be shocked if she did," she said emphatically. Then she sighed a long and painful sigh. "I just wish he could tell us. I hate this so much!"

In the back seat, Anthony listened to every word. He was so relieved his mother would come into the room next week. Hopefully she could see how horrible Cindy was and find him another therapist. He felt so trapped with Cindy. On the other hand, he learned the hard way that changing his therapists was never easy. And change didn't always mean better. He wondered how Cindy would act the next week. His head hurt from his smacking it. His stupid autistic head. It always messed him up.

23

Good Riddance

The following week, Anthony was apprehensive. He knew his mom would be in the room but his stomach did flips at the thought of facing Cindy. At home, he dashed madly around, touching random things. He wiped hand-lotion all over Harvey's back and on the sofa cushion. His mom scolded him while she cleaned up. They were both nervous about going back.

But when they got to the clinic Cindy was so charming and sweet she was like a talking marshmallow. Who was this person? Her laugh and cheerful voice made Anthony furious. Cindy praised him again and again during the session and gave him high-fives. Her smiles strained a face that was unaccustomed to looking pleasant. The situation was like a game and the winner was predetermined because Cindy, the faker, talked and he couldn't.

She took out her stack of flashcards to begin her receptive labels work. "Anthony, touch jacket," she said, never relaxing her face. She had sidelined her lollipop arsenal for now, relying instead on verbal encouragement alone.

Anthony easily understood what Cindy was -- a not very competent or talented practitioner who lacked patience and sensitivity. Talking, though, is power and he was totally trapped by his silence. He identified with the animals in a zoo. They too didn't talk and they had professionals guessing their needs. Their lives were unfulfilled and boring. A lion in a cage is never hungry but he also never satisfies his lion instinct to hunt or to chase. Anthony had a yearning, as profound as the lion's urge to stalk and catch prey, to participate in human life like a normal. Talking was the key. If he could talk, he could tell people his thoughts, show he was smart, play games, make friends, get an education that didn't teach him things he already knew. And get away from Cindy. Imagine that. If he could talk he would be free.

He touched the flashcard. Cindy high-fived him, glancing at Anthony's mom with a frozen smile.

His speech lessons were exercises in frustration. His apraxia trapped his tongue in ropes that bound it. *Move, move!* he'd plead with his tongue and mouth. The internal binds stayed tight and his utterances were unclear. His hands were not much better. People often asked his mother why she didn't teach him sign language. "It's hard for him," she'd answer.

Not hard. Impossible! Anthony would yell out in silence. *My hands are bound by the same internal rope that stops my tongue.* He longed to explain this to Cindy or Natasha but he couldn't, and so instead he listened to baby talk, "high five" and lectures about how his laziness or lack of motivation prevented him from becoming a talking boy.

He was a good listener. People who can't talk, but who hear everything, listen. So they learn. By overhearing conversations on every topic, Anthony was more aware than anyone gave him credit about current events, sports and autism theories. That's because he was inadvertently living the life of a fraud. His outside made him look like a randomly moving buffoon, his self-stimulatory behavior a kind of herky-jerky choreography. His rope-bound motor system obeyed the pointless commands of stims but somehow ignored the requests he consciously made for it to talk or write or even to give a relaxed smile on demand for a photo.

And Anthony listened to everything, though right now

he was trying not to listen to Cindy. She was explaining something to his mother about motivation, impulsivity, social behavior, mirror neurons and progress. It was very deep. Well, it was a break from flashcards. Cindy droned on and on and his mother listened politely. Anthony vanished into the table, rearranging the items she had placed so purposefully. She stopped talking and moved the items back to their proper positions. This redirected her attention to Anthony. She stared at his inattentive face and said, "Look at me," until she felt he was finally ready to tackle her stack of flashcards. The pile seemed a mile high. He stimmed with all his might, boycotting her, shaking his head, flapping his hands, disappearing her from his consciousness.

"You cannot be lazy like this if you want to talk," he heard her say yet again. Anthony knew he wasn't lazy. What she was asking of him was extraordinarily difficult. More difficult than anything she had ever done. In frustration, in anger, in desperation, Anthony grabbed Cindy's pale blue sweater and pulled it hard. A button flew off. She tried to pry his hands off but he wouldn't loosen.

"Anthony! Stop!" his mom yelled over and over until he finally let go.

That button turned out to be the excuse Cindy was looking for. Anthony's mother held him tightly on her lap. Cindy sighed deeply. It was time to break the news. Until Anthony wanted to speak, she told his mother, she believed his progress would remain stalled. He was very oppositional. She and Bonnie had discussed it with other therapists at the clinic. All of them were convinced that Anthony had no physiological reason to inhibit him from speaking. He could be a speaking boy. He *should* be a speaking boy. But his own behaviors consistently sabotaged progress. She and Bonnie had tried everything possible to reach him and they had decided together that Anthony should take a break from speech therapy altogether until he was more compliant.

"He's just not using his time productively," Cindy said, her face serious. "A temporary break may be beneficial to help him return fresh and ready to work."

"You want him to stop speech therapy?" his mother asked incredulously. *"That's* your recommendation?" She was dumbfounded and enraged. Anthony wasn't. He listened in delight. It was a dream come true. His passive aggressive war on Cindy was working!

"I disagree," his mother said firmly. It was up to her, wasn't it? "I'm willing to change his speech therapist though. Maybe you two aren't a good match. Anthony came out crying last week," she told Cindy. "Do you have any idea why?"

"No, I have no idea." Cindy turned pale. Her arms were now crossed tightly across her narrow chest. She pulled the hierarchy card. Bonnie, she said, had already expressed concerns that Anthony had plateaued in speech. She had hoped a new therapist might jumpstart him. "But it seems Anthony has no real interest in speaking more," she explained. "He seems to be satisfied in using pictograms and single word communication to meet his needs.

"I'm not suggesting giving up on speech therapy altogether," she added, clearly eager to end the session. "I'm recommending an interlude."

Anthony was laughing inside. *They want to have a break from me.* It made him happy to be a thorn in Cindy's side. On the other hand, he was distressed because his mother looked distressed. The irony, of course, was that he wanted to speak more than anything in the world. How stupid must Cindy be to think that he would prefer not to be able to communicate his ideas? *Sure, I have the potential to easily learn to talk, he thought, I just choose not to because it's so much fun being talked to in baby talk and led around like an ox, never able to let people know I'm intelligent. That makes sense. Anyone would choose to be lazy in speech therapy in order to keep **that** terrific situation going.*

"I need to talk to your supervisor," his mother said. She was usually calm. But now she looked livid. She was barely breathing.

"That would be Bonnie," Cindy replied in a saccharine tone, "and we both believe that this pause would be beneficial. But feel free to contact her." Anthony's mom grabbed her things to leave. Anthony followed. Then he stopped in the doorway and turned to offer Cindy some parting words.

You are boring and mean and a horrible speech therapist. I'm so happy to not work with you anymore, he said. Well, a boy can dream. He said it in his head, while jumping up and down on his toes. His mom took him by the hand, and that was the end of Cindy.

It was a good day. What Anthony didn't realize was that his darkest years would follow.

24

Lost Hope

Anthony had been an adorable child. Now he was an ungainly teenager. He moved awkwardly. He slouched and had soft muscles, a belly from Risperdal and a grumpy expression on his face. Five years had passed since Anthony had bid Cindy good riddance.

He was thirteen-years-old. He was in middle school now. No more Mrs. Lester. But not much else had changed. Anthony was in yet another self-contained autism class for non-speaking, low-functioning kids. Yes, he was definitely low-functioning. His parents had finally come to terms with that dire label. Dr. Hagerty had opened his mother's eyes to the truth. She had resisted accepting his point-of-view, but so much time had passed by now that she could no longer deny it. Anthony was not able to speak or write. He stimmed often and appeared lost in his own world, unable to understand language. But at school, they kept trying. He was still being taught kindergarten lessons in the hope that his comprehension skills might one day advance. Anthony was well past the brink of despair.

He had given up and it spiraled him downward, his temper short, his patience abandoned, his light dimmer. Dr. Hagerty helped the parents to accept that while his teaching approach was stellar, certain children remained intractable and uneducable because of the severity of their language processing problems or their low IQs. They simply had to be allowed to live as they were, assisted but unable to advance. How sad that Anthony, for whom he initially had such high hopes, had stagnated, and turned out to be one of them. Dr. Hagerty still met with the family occasionally but he no longer encouraged hope, or false hope, as he called it.

So they had abandoned their dreams. They had accepted, as Dr. Hagerty had advised. Living without hope was terrible. Anthony's parents had become sad and tired and Anthony had given up imagining that he one day might talk or even be able to show that he had a thinking mind. The days went on, dull and pointless. He treaded water, never moving forward.

There was now no reason to resist Autismland's allure. So Anthony gave in to his impulses. Why not indulge in fleeting stim sensations of pleasure? Anthony loved pouring uncooked rice through his fingers and watching it fall in noisy patterns. He gaped as he poured entire bottles of cranberry juice into the sink, watching it swirl down the drain in a stream of magenta. He loved stomping on the tube of hair conditioner in the shower to see the burst of hair product shoot out from the compressed plastic bottle.

He dismayed his family to distraction, wasting their money and looting their possessions. He couldn't stop. The obsessive-compulsive side of autism had risen in power as he grew older. He lacked the ability—for now—to defeat it, but he didn't truly care. He saw nothing but silence for him and baby talk from them and he had lost his interest in being an obedient little boy. The most troubling change, however, was that being a teenager meant that Anthony had lots of teenage angst. His body had the same moody hormonal surges as any other young man, the same desires for independence and friends. But he was stuck under piles of neurological trapdoors and he couldn't get out.

Mark was his idol. He was in high school. He had his learner's permit. He played soccer, had lots of friends and a busy social life. Mark was good-looking and athletic. He had friends contacting him constantly. He was a continuous reminder to Anthony that he had drawn the short stick in his genetic lottery. *I could have been like him if I didn't have autism*, Anthony thought, too often for his own emotional wellbeing. Nevertheless, Anthony knew that Mark was a kind, loving guy and he couldn't dislike him. He loved him despite feelings of jealousy and hopelessness. Gary, on the other hand, he could dislike. Gary was in the fifth grade. He loved his school, played youth volleyball and computer games. But he and Anthony rarely interacted directly unless Gary was telling Anthony to stop doing something annoying or inappropriate. They lived side by side under the same roof, but not together.

Harvey had died. It was the saddest day in Anthony's life. His whole family was broken-hearted but soon got another dog, a sensitive mutt named Dibby. Dibby had a pedigree of German Shepherd and no one knew what else, but she filled the Harvey-sized hole in everyone's hearts with her sweet nature. His parents still lived in the same house. They never got a bigger one. Anthony's mom had returned to working part-time. Everyone had moved on except Anthony.

Perhaps most frustrating, was that his parents, who loved him, still had to serve as his best friends because he had so few. Watching Mark and Gary go off with peers reminded Anthony of his own isolation and continued dependency on his parents. Anthony occasionally saw his own autistic peers, but only with his, and their, parents. He was never permitted the fresh breath of independence. Nor could he handle it if it became available. He was too impulsive. He had to fight urges and impulses all the time and he often lost the struggle, at times even grabbing his aide or his family members and pulling their hair in bursts of temper. Anthony began to fear his own desperation would eat him alive.

In his new classroom, Anthony had no textbooks or literature. He passed the time doing the same boring exercises he had done for years. It was not surprising that he sometimes lost his temper, that he stimmed most of the day. Autismland was his only respite. But his near-total retreat cut him off from the outside world in a deep and lonely way. He prayed often as he lay in bed at night to find a means to communicate. But his tongue was cleaved and his hands bound. He wondered sometimes if his silent prayers were even heard.

His teacher, Miss Lang, primarily saw her job as being a kindly warehouse warden. She was bubbly and her high-pitched voice squeaked enthusiasm. Her students stimmed, yelled, had fits, picked their noses. It was a bedlam she faced bravely as she organized the students, urging them to sit quietly in their seats, trying gamely to engage them. Her lessons focused on elementary reading. Her hand pointed to the letters she had written on the board, e-g-g, c-o-o-k-i-n-g, s-a-l-t-y. Anthony looked at the pictures of the vocabulary words and forced his mind to fly away. He longed to sit in a regular classroom.

His classmates were as trapped as he was. Hugo had loud shrieking tantrums daily. He had low frustration tolerance and high sensory overload. Carlos had problems sitting in his seat. His kinesthetic needs were intensely compelling and he bounced vigorously on the giant ball in the corner. Kenny stimmed constantly, bumping, rocking, rubbing his skin, lining up toys, playing with his saliva. Robert had limpid fingers and moved his soft body slowly. The lone girl, Susie, weighed two hundred pounds, a byproduct of her medication. None of the students could communicate verbally or nonverbally, yet in his heart Anthony believed that each one was like him, that each one had an intact mind trapped in his or her own body and that the body did its best to make the occupant look absent.

Looking into the room the average viewer might be perplexed by the students' weird behavior, not knowing that they struggled to cope with background noise, motor urges, boredom, frustration, sensory overload and compulsive commands from their nervous systems. Yet a careful viewer—if any existed—would have seen beyond the omnipresent low expectations that permeated the room, beyond mere symptoms and autistic behaviors. While the students' bodies disobeyed, ran amuck and looked stupid, their eyes showed what their bodies could not. In these real "windows of opportunity," clear glimpses of intentionality appeared, however briefly, skittering across their faces in an instant before autism took over again. In those moments, the students' eyes sometimes revealed their true pain, hurt and frustration. Their own arms and legs, their own mouths and hands were the faithless betrayers of their minds, but sometimes their eyes told the story. As Anthony's mother had said years before, "There are glimmers of understanding, but they pass too quickly for me to be certain."

Sadly, there were no careful viewers in Anthony's world. For him, this was the 'give-up' room. Days and weeks turned to years. Then, one Friday, not long before Anthony's sixteenth birthday, everything changed.

Part II

"How wonderful that we have met this paradox. Now we have some hope of making progress."

Niels Bohr

25

Chasing Cures

"**H**ave you heard about this lady who teaches autistic kids to communicate by typing?" Robin asked Anthony's mother. As usual, his mom was multi-tasking, at once sorting the laundry, baking a lasagna and talking to Robin on the phone.

"Oh yeah, I saw her on the news. I don't know. Seems improbable to me," she said while fishing out a pair of Gary's socks from the pile.

"We've tried literally everything else," Robin said a bit defensively. "What do we have to lose here?"

"I know what Natasha would say. Smoke and mirrors." Anthony's mom sighed. "If he could communicate, wouldn't someone have discovered it by now?" She found another pair of socks. When Robin didn't reply, she kept talking. "How does someone who can't understand language type like an adult? I mean, Anthony can't even read yet. I think it must be a scam."

"I'm going to try it," Robin said firmly. "I have to see for myself if it's for real or if she's doing voodoo or some kind of puppet show."

"I wouldn't waste my time on it. Or my money." Anthony's mother tucked the phone in the crook of her neck while she carried the hamper to Gary's room.

"Nice open mind there," Robin sighed. "I guess I'll have to keep it secret from you." They both laughed.

Anthony's mom hung up the phone and thought about how Robin chased after every promising claim out there. Her success rate was poor. David had moved in with his grandfather because she could no longer manage his outbursts. He had grown tall and unpredictable and she wasn't able to physically control him when he erupted. For now, her father could handle him. It gave Robin the bandwidth she needed to try yet another long-shot snake-oil treatment. Anthony's mom figured it had about as much chance of working on David as the brain diet, chelation, hormone injections, mega-dose vitamins, anti-fungal, music and vision treatments Robin had tried. They all began with much hoopla and lots of recommendation testimonials from thrilled parents. And they cost Robin bushels of money. When Anthony's mom asked her if a given treatment had worked she would reply, "I think so," in an optimistic tone of voice. Then she would add, "It's hard to tell though. I thought his eye contact was a little better," or "I thought his speech was clearer," or, "I think his attention span is longer." But in the end, Robin was always frustrated. They talked about it so often.

Anthony's mom was more pragmatic and she thought Robin was living on unicorn planet with rainbows and pipedreams. Anthony's mom pragmatically believed in the course she had taken, the scientific path, the Hagerty way. The fact that it hadn't helped Anthony much did not invalidate its efficacy. After all, many kids—look at Peter, for example—had thrived under Hagerty's guidance. Anthony just didn't seem to have it in him to progress. His autism was just too severe. Her heart broke for Robin, who still chased what she would never find. She imagined their follow up call.

"How was it?"

"Interesting."

"Do you think it helped David?"

Hesitating, "I think so." Pause. "It's hard to say. Maybe a little. I think he's trying harder to communicate now."

Anthony's mom sighed. She hurt in anticipation for Robin.

26

Plate Tectonics

Five months later, when Anthony came home from school, he found Robin at his house. His school bus dropped him at his door and both mothers met him outside. Mark was there too. He was a student in community college, still living at home while he studied and saved tuition money before transferring to university. He was working part-time in a bicycle store, repairing bikes and trying to amass some savings. All of them were looking at Anthony strangely. "Hi, Anthony!" his mom sang, trying to sound upbeat. He could hear her voice tremble a little. Mark was looking at Anthony intensely but he was talking to their mother.

"Mom, do you remember when you were reading the *Little House* books to us and Anthony hid under his blanket?" he said in a low but insistent voice. "I want to try this." They all clustered weirdly around Anthony, led him in the front door and hovered near him while he ate his snack at the kitchen table. There was eagerness in the air. They wanted him to finish quickly. Anthony wondered what was up.

The instant Anthony finished eating they brought him to the dining room table. His mom sat to his right. Excitedly she thrust a laminated alphabet chart in front of him. Anthony had no idea what she expected him to do. "Hi Anthony, what's your favorite color?" she asked, holding the board in front of him. He just sat there, unable to respond. She persisted. "What did you do in school today?" He sat, arm unmoving, then tried to get up and leave. Mark encouraged him to remain in his seat.

"I think you're jumping in too fast," Robin observed. "I

mean, Marina doesn't start this like that. She didn't even use a full board at first."

"Let me try," Mark said. His mother reluctantly got up and switched places with her oldest son. Mark sat next to Anthony and started talking to him. He said, "Listen Anthony, you're probably wondering what the hell we're doing." He very consciously did not dumb down his language. "Robin has been bringing David to this lady, Marina, who teaches autistic people to communicate and answer questions by touching letters on a board. So, we saw a video of David touching the board and it was really cool and we wanted to see if you could do this too."

Anthony heard the words in disbelief. He was full of contradictory emotions. On the one hand, he had the feeling that his prayers were being answered and that this was his chance to show he was intelligent to his loved ones. On the other hand, he was terrified that if he failed the test he might never have another opportunity. He had no confidence in his body obeying him. Just then, Gary entered the room.

"What are you doing?" He watched the scene curiously.

"Later, Gary," Mark hissed. He didn't want the momentum broken.

"What's your problem? Why don't you just answer me?" Gary protested, fed up with Mark's perpetual impatience with him.

Robin said in a soft voice, "We're trying something new with Anthony to help his communication." This held no interest for Gary, so he left the room, to Anthony's relief. Mark turned to his brother.

"Anthony, can you spell 'Anthony?'" He waited expectantly. Anthony did nothing. He felt panicky. Anthony knew he had to do something. His brain screamed at his hand to move. His hand ignored him. Mark looked frustrated.

"Come on, Anthony. Touch something." He picked up his brother's flaccid hand and pulled it to the board.

His mother said, "I don't think he knows what you want."

Robin added, "Maybe Marina will have more luck." She was standing behind his chair.

"No, Robin, that makes no sense," Anthony's mother replied. "He either has the skill or he doesn't. If he can't do it with me or Mark, why would he be able to do it with her? I saw what she did with David. It looked convincing, but Anthony isn't David. It's not in him." Her words terrified Anthony.

Mark turned to his mother. "Mom, you're being such a defeatist," he said. "It's only been five minutes. It must not be easy. If it were easy, don't you think he'd be doing it already?"

"Mark, you're not being realistic."

"Mom, can I please try?" As Mark and mom sparred, Anthony was already fleeing the table. He walked into the family room, where Gary was watching television and started dancing in front of it, flicking his fingers intensely, obscuring Gary's view.

"Do what you want," his mom said, "but don't torture the poor kid, and make sure you're not unconsciously moving his arm because you want this so much. You know, there's this whole controversy going on about facilitated communication."

Robin kept her mouth shut. She had been friends with Anthony's mom too long to get into a conflict. His mom felt disappointed. Her intuition told her not to trust this rainbow unicorn from Robin-land, but she also got chills remembering the video of David and how he answered Marina's questions, his finger touching the correct letters. She had watched it closely, over and over. It wasn't obvious how Marina was getting David to answer her.

Anthony was now stimming feverishly. He bounced up and down behind the curtains, a portal to Autismland where he hoped he might find an escape from his anxiety. His mother saw him and gave him a tablet playing his favorite cartoons. She hoped it would help him calm down quickly. Meanwhile, Mark announced that he was going for a run. He needed to blow off some steam his way. As Anthony lulled himself with the familiar videos, Robin and Anthony's mother sat down in the dining room to talk.

"You know, Marina doesn't start like this," Robin said, trying to be encouraging without pressing Anthony's mom too hard. "She uses lessons. She has methods to encourage the breakthrough. It's a gradual process. And you know David's still learning. He's not fluent like her daughter is." She put the alphabet board on the table.

"Is she the only person David can communicate with like this?" Anthony's mom asked. She felt disappointed by her unsuccessful experiment with Anthony. It reminded her not to ask for stars. They were too far out of reach.

"For now, yes." Robin stared at the letter board.

Skepticism filled Anthony's mother's eyes. She seemed exasperated. "Robin, I want to believe in it, but it makes no sense to me. People have worked with Anthony his whole life. Why hasn't one of them ever mentioned this? Why have they all told me that he doesn't understand? There's this one lady and the entire professional community thinks she's nuts. What am I supposed to think, Robin?" She got up and brought a bowl of grapes to the table.

"Think plate tectonics," Robin blurted.

"Huh?"

"One lone scientific voice against everybody else. Lots of theories have been proven wrong in history." Robin pressed on.

"Yes, I know, but this is hardly plate tectonics." There was a brief silence while the moms ate their grapes. Robin broke it.

"Are you a refrigerator mother?" she asked pointedly.

"What are you talking about?"

"Did you cause Anthony's autism because you were a cold bitch of a mother? That's what everyone used to think." She looked at her friend.

"No one believes that anymore," Anthony's mom replied emphatically.

"Exactly. But in the fifties, everyone did. In the fifties, you can bet that everyone thought that autism was an emotional disturbance *we* caused. I love Jason and reject David. That's why David *chooses* to be autistic. Does that even make any sense?"

"No, it doesn't."

"But every brilliant mind thought it was true, okay?" Robin's cheeks flushed.

"You can't compare that to today," Anthony's mom said, exhaling loudly. "Our understanding is more scientific now."

"Well, what if it's wrong?"

"How is that possible? How could *everyone* be wrong?"

"I don't know." Robin was defiant now. She knew how much she didn't know. And that was the point. "Maybe parts are wrong. But now I know David is smart. I know he has feelings. I believe that it's his body, not his mind that's messing him up."

Anthony's mom's eyes filled with tears. She suddenly had a sliver of hope, an emotion she had abandoned, and it frightened her. She began to weep. Robin hugged her, her thin, tiny frame offering a mountain of strength. Outside the room, Anthony paced the hall, listening to every word and he could see hope like a light turning on. It was out of his reach, but once again it existed.

27

Not Possible

That evening Anthony's father watched the video of David. He sat in his favorite recliner, his arms uncomfortably folded across his chest. "I'm not convinced," he asserted in a strong voice.

"Convinced of what?" Mark asked, pressing his father.

"Come on, Mark, you know David. Do you really think he has the capacity to communicate like that?" He raised the footrest on his chair and leaned back, as if the action signified that the discussion was over. It wasn't.

"He is, though," Mark replied.

"I'll believe it if he does it when he's alone."

Mark rolled his eyes. "How can he communicate if he's alone? Who would he talk to?"

Mark was very tenacious. His dad realized he would have to lay out the facts. "Mark, you're not looking at this scientifically. If he has the skill he should be able to do it any place, any time. I think she must be using some séance moves on him, or something." It came off as a bit condescending even though that's not what he intended.

"Dad," Mark said a little impatiently, "watch it again. She doesn't even touch him and she doesn't tell him the letters to touch."

"Maybe. It's impossible to say. She holds the letter board. Who's to say how she prompts him."

"That's ridiculous. He's obviously answering her questions." Mark's voice was edgy now.

"Look Mark, I know you want to believe. Maybe he got the

questions before. Maybe they trained him to reply. You have to take anything Robin says with a grain of salt. How many cures has she found already? Mark, come on, use your head." Anthony's father didn't realize it, but with that, he had thrown down a gauntlet. Mark staked out his position. He was a man now, too, and he had learned that the only way to defeat his father was by overpowering him with facts.

"Fine, Dad, I'll try on my own, okay?"

"Okay, Mark," his dad said a bit sarcastically. "The researchers have got to hand it to you. Dr. Hagerty's lifetime of expertise defers to you."

"You said yourself Hagerty was a jerk." Mark's lips were drawn in a tight line. Anthony didn't see Dr. Hagerty anymore. He went to another psychiatrist for medication monitoring, one less expensive and closer to home. But the great doctor still held sway over Anthony's parents' thinking.

"I said he was full of himself. Interpersonally he is a jerk, but he does believe in scientific methodology. He's backed by data and research. This Marina is backed by what? Robin? Let her prove it if it's for real."

Mark was now in full pitbull mode. "If she proves it, will you believe it?" he challenged his father.

"Let her do studies like he has. Let her prove it with data."

"How many studies has Hagerty done? Can you show me?" Mark countered.

His dad was now sitting up in his chair, giving the argument his full attention. "I know he has done studies. I know she hasn't."

"So you can see with your own eyes that David is pointing to letters on the board to make words, but there's no study on it, so he's not really doing it?"

"Mark, knock it off. I believe skepticism is warranted here."

"I agree Dad. I'm skeptical—of Hagerty's claims of curing people."

"For God's sake, Mark. He cured Peter."

"Yes, but not your own son." Mark was getting to the heart of the issue now. "My question is, were they the same to start? Maybe what Peter had was curable with Hagerty's methods and maybe what Anthony and David have isn't."

"They all have autism, Mark."

Anthony was eavesdropping, pacing ten feet away, just out of sight. He wanted to catch every word. He felt his heart racing.

"Yes, but maybe not the same autism," Mark suggested. "I think at least you need to keep an open mind about this."

"I'll keep an open mind, but I don't believe in magic."

Mark turned and saw his brother standing in the hallway. Anthony was holding the letter board and waving it furiously. His dad saw Anthony, too. But each interpreted the scene differently. The father saw his son, once again, fascinated with movement and stimming on the nearest object he could find, in this case the laminated letter board Robin had left behind on the dining room table. Mark firmly believed that Anthony was trying to tell him he wanted to try the letter board. He thought Anthony was excited about the prospect, but unable to control his movements.

One of them was right.

28

Hope

That night Anthony lay in bed imagining that there was possibility for him. He was not used to feeling this way. His entire life he had hoped to speak verbally but he knew this likelihood was nearly nonexistent. He had the ability to croak out some memorized words and brief phrases, but only trained ears could understand them. It was obvious to him that speech would never allow him to show others that he understood. And since speech was the only faulty avenue available to him, he was locked inside.

Ages ago, he imagined that he might use sign language to communicate, but his fingers were too inept. Though Anthony was now sixteen, his baseball mitt hands still fumbled while opening chips or tying shoes and they were useless for gesturing his intentions. Meanwhile, his handwriting looked like cryptic hieroglyphics written by a chicken. Once he had dreamed of handwriting his thoughts, but his ability to initiate the necessary movements from thought to hand was so faulty he could not, so his repertoire of chicken scratches mostly consisted of copying things. It dismayed him that his body's limitations had no intention of revealing what was inside him. He had hoped most of his life to find a way out, but eventually he became apathetic. He had never proved his intelligence in his discrete trials nor in his school. He had figured for years that he would end up like David, living on stims, living away from home.

But now David was coming home. He had calmed down considerably since he started working with Marina. He was so much happier. Robin believed she could handle him now, especially as their communication improved. She had even begun thinking that eventually David might be able to transition into general education. True, Anthony's parents thought this laughable, but Anthony tried not to think of their skepticism. He figured that David's skills pointing and even typing would improve with time. If David succeeded, then there would be hope for him too.

Anthony thought about what Mark had said to his father about Dr. Hagerty. He didn't like to go there. But now, he remembered clearly the day he fully came to understand what he was up against. He was little, only around nine-years-old. He knew what Dr. Hagerty was like in his private sessions, but on this day Anthony fully realized how Dr. Hagerty had influenced and shaped the theories and attitudes that controlled his life. His mom had been reading aloud to his father from a decades-old interview with Dr. Hagerty that had originally appeared in a prominent psychology magazine. She had found it on the Internet. As he often did, Anthony listened from the next room, pacing in tight rows.

"I can tell you that these children look normal," she read. "Some are quite beautiful."

"That's true, she remarked as an aside to her husband. "Anthony's gorgeous."

"But in fact, they are not children at the truest level," she read on, as if Anthony couldn't possibly hear what she read, or if he did, understand her words. As if he were a pacing, earless cloud. "Do not let their beauty fool you into imagining that a normal child lives trapped within. Simply, they are as autistic on the inside as they are on the outside. The behavior you see reflects an inner panorama of confusion. These children are pure id living in a world that is incomprehensible."

"What a way of putting it," she said.

"Go on," her husband prodded.

She continued. "Imagine you are a young child and your mother tells you, 'Put your shoes on' and your mind hears incoherent gobbledygook, unable to tease out words from a blur of sounds. I liken it to arriving in a country where you cannot understand one word of the language. How can you discern where one word ends and the next begins? But for an autistic child the situation is even more challenging, because *you* are aware that labels exist: nouns, verbs, adjectives, and grammar. Many autistic children have none of that. They live in a world devoid of conceptual language, unless we painstakingly teach it to them one label at a time through operant conditioning. If we get them young, ideally under three, the plastic brain may be molded into normalcy. It is important to start as young as possible, before it is too late."

His mom stopped reading the papers she had printed. "Do you think we started him too late?" she asked.

"He wasn't even three," her husband said.

"I don't know. I wish we had started him at one."

Pacing, eavesdropping, nine-year-old Anthony had unfortunately understood most of Hagerty's pronouncements. Though he didn't yet know what 'id,' meant, he certainly understood the implications and he knew real gobbledygook when he heard it.

Now, all these years later, Anthony lay in bed thinking about the power theories had held over his life and, in particular, the power of Dr. Hagerty's ideas. He fantasized about what he would like to tell Dr. Hagerty and composed a mental letter. Dear *Dr. Hagerty*, it said, *Shut up! Shut up! Shut up! Sincerely, Anthony*. It was amusing to envision Hagerty's mouth open, shocked to get a letter Anthony had written. He figured Hagerty would read it with a scowl. He would adjust his reading glasses, just as Anthony had seen him do so many times in his office, and look carefully at the words.

"No, communication at this level is simply impossible," Anthony imagined him muttering. "I know this Anthony. Sadly, he is the type we refer to as 'low-functioning.' To communicate with this kind of focused anger would require theory of mind and Anthony has no conceptualization that others have ideas unlike his own. In fact, people are merely objects to him. I therefore reject this letter."

Anthony imagined Dr. Hagerty sitting down to write him back. "Say hi, Anthony! Good job! High five! Touch envelope! Touch angry! Touch your nose! Open up, here comes a gummy bear! Say bye!" Even Anthony's revenge fantasies turned against him.

Anthony's bed creaked as he rolled back and forth, restless. He thought more about what had happened that day: Robin's visit, the news about David, his mother's tears, his brother's faith in him. Anthony had never imagined pointing to letters to communicate. It had never occurred to him that touching letters on a board or electronic device might be a vehicle for sharing his thoughts. He lacked the ability now, not to spell, but to use his eyes to scan an array of letters and to move his index finger and arm the way he needed them to move to be able to communicate like that.

If possible, David's motor system was even more fouled up than his, but David had learned to move his finger to the letters on the alphabet board and to answer questions in full sentences and he was beginning to learn how to use a keyboard. It made Anthony wonder if he might be able to do that too if he got the proper instruction. He had mixed emotions because he knew Mark believed in him but that his parents were not going to change their long-held views. He wasn't sure they would pursue this and he feared that Mark had no idea how to approach it, despite his good intentions. Anthony lacked confidence in himself after so many years of failure. And yet... hope still enticed him. Could he dare hope? Would he be disappointed yet again? Wouldn't indifference and apathy not be safer, more logical for a person in his situation? He tossed and turned, vocalizing in bed, unable to unwind. He imagined himself free but he was terrified that he dared to imagine.

29

Tension

There was tension in the air in Anthony's home. Marina hung over the family like a specter. His father wished he had never heard of that kook. He was irritated that Robin had brought this inanity into his home. He was irritated with his wife for being emotional. He was irritated with Mark for being obstreperous. He was irritated with Anthony for being autistic. The only family members he wasn't irritated with were Gary and the dog. These days, the family never mentioned Marina.

He took Gary out for some ice cream. They talked about going camping, about Gary's crazy Spanish teacher and whether they would ever try bungee jumping. Never Marina. That evening, Anthony's father sat in his recliner reading news on his laptop. He believed his conversation with Mark had been the final word on the subject, but Mark took it as a challenge.

Mark approached his father. "Hey Dad, I did a little research." He was about to overpower with facts. "Do you know how many studies Dr. Hagerty has done?" His father looked tired. He really didn't want to have this conversation.

"Drop it, Mark."

"I thought you'd like to know." He pressed on. "He did one. More than forty years ago. One study, Dad, and there's some saying that his sample was skewed, like he only worked with kids like Peter and he dropped the kids like Anthony and David." His father sat silently. Finally, he spoke.

"Where did you read that?" Mark cited the source. "Is that a reputable source? It seems inconceivable to me. I'm sure there must be more studies."

"I think there are studies, but not by him. No one has come close to his success rate in later studies." Mark looked at his father. "Thought you'd like to know," he said quietly.

His father rubbed his forehead as if he was trying to make sense of what he had just heard. "I'll look into it," he said finally. He seemed anxious suddenly. Fourteen years of faith in one man's theories was hitting its first roadblock. Perhaps, if he were honest with himself, it was the second roadblock. The first was the realization that Anthony had progressed so little, even though the family had complied for years and years with every program and every promise. He had accepted that. You win some, you lose some. But never had he doubted the methods.

He snapped his laptop closed and turned on the television looking for a distraction but it didn't work, so he reopened his laptop and went to the site Mark mentioned. There he read about a young Hagerty, boy genius professor, almost fifty years earlier, using cattle prods and other "aversives" on autistic self-abusers. Hagerty accompanied his electric shocks with slaps and in-your-face military screaming. Of course, these treatments were long abandoned, the stick replaced entirely by the carrot, and no longer discussed by his followers, who insisted emphasis be placed solely on the many doors of insight Hagerty had opened.

Hagerty's realization that autism was neurological and not a catastrophic emotional shutting down of oneself because of mean mothers had improved the lives of those wretches in state hospitals who had been locked away, tied up and forgotten. It was essential to overlook his questionable early methods because he had helped so many more individuals than he had hurt. His insights had shaped lives for the better. And his methods, refined and formalized, ultimately became big business. Every pediatrician told parents to pursue it. Agencies sprang up like weeds, college students studied how to hold flashcards, say, "good job," and eventually open agencies of their own. And thousands of kids like Anthony started at the age of two, hour after hour drilling their way to normalcy. Dr. Hagerty's followers were incredibly devoted. Any hint of criticism of him or his methods was met with raging Internet vituperation.

Parents with a newly diagnosed toddler look for hope and the pediatrician gives it with a recommendation for intensive, scientific behavioral treatment. The program is professionally run, the lesson plans are organized to the tiniest degree, the confidence is high, the Barbies eager and energetic. So, parents like Anthony's march on like good little soldiers, even though their beloved child isn't progressing much and no one asks why. The only changes are tweaks to the programmatic lessons. The failure, as everybody knows, is in a kid like Anthony himself, not in the program. Not everyone responds to good medicine.

Peter's family had the opposite experience, of course. He thrived. He talked. He learned at least ten times faster than Anthony. He got what he needed from the program and his family loved it, grateful every day for Peter's rapid progression. He was a success. He was living proof of the genius of Dr. Hagerty. True, Peter's speech was a bit robotic-like and, true, he was still a few beats off the norm. But he had been able to integrate into a regular school and a regular class. He could go anywhere and not be stared at. He looked and acted mostly normally and his parents absolutely knew that he would have been like Anthony without Dr. Hagerty. Yet, Anthony was like Anthony *with* Dr. Hagerty. He and his family had followed Hagerty's and Natasha's guidance to the letter.

Anthony's father looked at the articles and thought back to when Anthony was small. It had been the most overwhelming time in his life. He had two small boys, he and his wife had just found out she was pregnant with their third, and then they learned that Anthony had a life-altering condition that was incurable. Meanwhile the books painted a terrible future for Anthony. He would 'be indifferent to others.' He didn't 'think in language.' He had 'no desire to be touched,' (evidence be damned). On and on, the books told them that Anthony was a hopeless case. He was permanently autistic.

But behaviorism offered a lifeline of promise. A hope of recovery. He and his wife had embraced the promise, accepted its disruption in their lives, so many hours every week, hoping, hoping, until hope ran out. Anthony's father now wondered why they had been so loyal. Once one starts on a path it's hard to change. He had eyes to see how Anthony was doing. He saw the possibilities of recovery receding, yet he and his wife marched on, until Anthony got too big and too old to do flashcards anymore.

Anthony rarely saw Natasha now. She had started her own autism agency, like so many ambitious behaviorists and they had remained faithful to her. She supplied Anthony's school aide and the aide's supervisor, and she no longer worked directly with the kids. But Anthony's parents talked to her occasionally when they had big concerns, and she continued to encourage them with tips. His father had never doubted, never veered in his thinking. Not until this moment. Like Anthony, he was frightened to hope. Hopes have a way of getting dashed in Autismland.

Next, he turned to Marina's webpage and looked at video after video of severely autistic youths stimming, moving awkwardly, vocalizing and yet seemingly typing on their own using a keyboard or iPad, or pointing to letters on a cardboard, laminated letter board. He studied the videos, searching for the trick she used. The obviously low-functioning boy answered profound questions about the lesson she taught. Impossible. It was impossible. The boy simply looked too weird, too random to be intelligent.

Anthony's father's mind rejected what he saw. Even though he saw no tricks, he saw no intelligence either. There was no way that boy understood. There was no way he could answer complex questions about science. It had to be coached or camera trickery. Yet, if coaching was the thing going on, didn't that reveal intelligence of a sort? He imagined auditory prompts he couldn't hear or visual prompts he couldn't see telling the boy to type "helium," or "neon," or "hydrogen" to questions regarding the Periodic Table. Was he really supposed to believe that this kid understood chemistry? "Give me a break," he thought. "Anthony has no clue how to tie his own shoes."

He watched again and again, growing more frustrated because he could not see how the kids were manipulated. He searched the Internet for critiques of Marina's methods. Simply Googling her name immediately brought up the search bar "Marina Folvino hoax." One article claimed that the kids were not autistic. Another claimed she had invisible prompts. Her methods were hands-on and intrusive, the critics proclaimed, inserting the bias of the instructor into the session. She was labeled "dangerous" and "unscientific" and accused of preying on the desperation of parents. He felt better knowing he wasn't alone in his skepticism.

He got up and walked to the dining room table, where Anthony was stimming on his iPad. His father looked at him for a long time. Finally, he asked, "Anthony, do you understand?" He watched his son carefully. Anthony had looked at him briefly. "Can you close that for a second?" he asked. He moved the iPad out of Anthony's reach, put a large children's book about animals in front of his son and opened it. There was a lizard on one page, a rodent on the other. "Which one is the lizard?" he asked. Anthony looked at the wall and flicked his fingers. "Oh, forget it," his dad mumbled. "I must be losing my mind."

30

Mark Tries

The next day Robin's phone rang while she was shopping for groceries. It was Mark. "Hi, Robin," he stammered, feeling a bit awkward calling his mother's friend without her knowledge. "Listen, I was wondering if I could come some time to see Marina work with David. Would that be okay?" Robin listened as she put a bag of Granny Smith apples into the cart. She was in a hurry. Why hadn't she just let the call go to voicemail?

"It's fine with me. I need to check with Marina first though," she answered, distractedly. Then she paused for a moment, thinking. "Is your mom coming too?"

Mark spoke quietly into the phone, "Um, I'm not telling her. Or my dad."

"Maybe you should," she replied, realizing uncomfortably that Mark was acting on his own, against his parents' wishes. Robin scanned the shelves searching for her favorite raisin bread. "I don't want to get in the middle of something."

"Oh sure, okay. Never mind. Thanks anyway." Mark hung up abruptly, unsure what to do next. He knew he was on his own with this. He went to his room and looked at the videos on Marina's webpage, the same ones his father had pored over the night before. They showed her working with many different people with autism. Her clients had a varying severity of symptoms and a range of different behaviors and challenges, but they all obviously had severe autism. Mark noticed that they had different levels of fluency typing. Some could use a keyboard or iPad. Some used alphabet boards.

Some used word prediction successfully. Some barely used the board to spell one word. He saw that the kids were concentrating hard and working hard. None could type with more than one finger.

To keep them focused and hitting the keys, Marina peppered them with constant encouragement and verbal prompts to keep going or to look at all the letters on the board. But she never told them to touch a particular letter, and she didn't move their hands around. Mark saw that Marina's lessons had no candy treats or high fives. He noticed that she spoke normally to her students. Her language was respectful, and despite how many stims and oddities she faced, the lesson she gave was age appropriate. He found it fascinating. He noticed that Marina's behavior assumed her students could think and understand. She then taught them interesting things and discussed those lessons. This was the opposite of how Anthony had been taught.

Mark had no idea if Marina was nuts or a con artist, which his father suspected. Mark had always thought Anthony had more intelligence than he got credit for, that he had some kind of internal blockage that prevented him from showing it. He imagined how frustrating life must be to a person who understands, but is viewed by everyone as someone who does not. He imagined never speaking his whole life, never sharing an idea, thought or preference, never socializing, going out the way he did with friends, playing sports. He felt sad thinking about it.

Mark wanted to try to use the letter board Robin had left behind again. He watched the videos closely so he could try to copy some of Marina's methods. He looked at his own textbooks for a lesson and decided there was no way he could use them. Anthony had never even had one academic lesson in his life. How was he supposed to be able to deal with college work? He went to Gary's room and grabbed Gary's science and history books. They were still ridiculously advanced compared to what Anthony was being taught in class but at least the material was simpler than his own textbooks. After skimming through the books for a while he opted for a lesson on desert ecosystems.

"The hot, dry weather in the desert ecosystem creates unique challenges for the plants and animals that live there. With little annual rainfall, all desert life has developed a variety of specialized adaptations to survive the extremes of daytime heat, cold nights and long, dry spells. Nighttime in the desert is often below freezing and daytime temperatures frequently rise to above 38 degrees Celsius (100 degrees Fahrenheit), yet the greatest challenge for desert life is scarcity of water.

When one thinks of desert flora, the image of a prickly cactus often comes to mind. These intriguing plants have features that enable them to conserve what little water is available. Their shallow root systems spread widely, allowing for quick absorption of any rainfall."

Mark wondered if reading about deserts, cacti and ecosystems with Anthony was preposterous wishful thinking on his part. Still, he figured he had nothing to lose by trying. If he failed, Anthony would be no worse off than he was right now and if he succeeded he might be better off.

Anthony, who had been anticipating that something like this might come up, felt differently. He knew that if he failed, his parents might never again consider teaching him to communicate by typing. The gap between what they saw in his movements, his bizarre behavior, his flat, expressionless face and his ineptitude contrasted too much with the idea that he had a working brain. He knew that to them, this was like asking a scientist to believe in magic, so he felt very nervous when Mark came to get him. For Mark, what they were about to do was an exercise, even an experiment, and Mark, who always loved science, enjoyed experiments. For Anthony, it was life or death. Freedom or prison. He began stimming to calm down.

Mark sat Anthony at his desk. Anthony impulsively began picking up objects: the stapler, tape dispenser, paper clips. Mark cleared the desktop off.

"Okay, Anthony, it's no big deal. Chill out, okay? I know you're smart. I believe in you, so let's just try. I don't know what I'm doing, so we can hopefully figure this out together." This short speech comforted Anthony. He knew that more than anyone else in his family, Mark had always suspected that Anthony had more going on internally than he showed.

Mark read aloud the passage about the desert. Anthony listened. Mark asked, "What's the climate like in a desert?" He wondered if 'climate' was too hard a word to use. Anthony didn't move. He felt paralyzed with anxiety. Mark persisted. He remembered that Marina often gave choices. "Is it hot and dry or cold in a desert?" he looked at Anthony, who was trying to stim to escape his distress. Anthony thought about his, "What weather is it today?" drills and how much he detested them throughout elementary school. He thought about rebelling, or fleeing, or just living forever in silence and isolation. He decided he had to try. He had to. He wasn't being drilled on his understanding of the weather; it was an actual lesson from a textbook.

Mark pulled Anthony's index finger out and tucked his other fingers in, molding his hand into a pointing shape. Anthony tried to get started. He really wanted to answer the question. But he was stuck. It was like his hand was frozen. His expletive, horrible, useless hand! Mark grabbed his hand.

"Come on, Anthony!" He put it on the letter 'h'. He said, "Now you go on." He let go of Anthony's hand and Anthony, on his own, somehow moved it to the 'o.' Somehow, the motor blockage seemed to unfreeze in his nervous system when Mark started him off. His hand had obeyed him. Mark said "o" out loud after Anthony touched the letter just as he had observed Marina do, so Anthony knew his big brother had seen him touch it.

"What's next?" Mark prompted, imitating Marina. Slowly Anthony found the 't'. Mark said, "Hot. That's right."

Mark tried to hide his emotions. He wanted to whoop and jump up but he contained himself. He asked, "Okay, what's another climactic condition in the desert besides hot?" He spoke to Anthony as if he was intelligent and Anthony knew that Mark knew. It gave him confidence. Holding the letter board in front of Anthony, Mark waited. Finally, he grabbed Anthony's hand and started him off again, touching the 'd'. He watched, amazed, as his brother completed the word, 'r, y."

"Dry. Right, a desert is hot and dry. Okay, one more question. Name a plant adapted to desert life." He put the board in front of Anthony but didn't start him this time. "Come on, you can do it. Look at the letters." Despite his excitement, Mark tried to remain the picture of calm. He thought if he pushed, Anthony would get anxious. He repeated the question. "What plant is it? It has thorns." Anthony managed to lift his hand and touched the letter next to the 'c.' "No, the letter next to it," Mark said. "You have to touch the right letter." Anthony faltered, hitting near, not on the c three times. "You can do it," Mark coaxed. "Move your hand to the left."

Anthony was trying so hard he could feel his brain straining. He had promised himself he would try in spite of his nervousness, but in that moment, he broke that promise.

His nervousness rose too high, too quickly for him to stop. Panic crashed all over him. He jumped up, grabbed Mark and began yelling and flailing around. He bolted the room. In his panic, he bumped into the dining room table and hurt his hip. He yelled and jumped up and down, flapping his hands. Thought had fled. He was in full lizard brain mode. Fight or flight impulses overtook him.

Their mother approached, her face showing concern. "What's going on? Why is Anthony having a tantrum?" she shouted. Mark stayed away. He knew his mother would be angry that he had upset Anthony. She brought Anthony his stim toys but he was too excited to use them. Anthony grabbed her arm tightly.

"No, Anthony," she yelled, "All done!" She pushed him into his room and closed his door. He never tried to flee once he was in his room. No one knew why. Anthony paced and paced, walking his reasoning brain back into his consciousness. What had he done? Mark would never try again. Why was his brain his enemy? He wanted to show he was smart so badly. His body conspired against him, his mind overloaded too fast, his emotional self-regulation was too primitive. He felt so sad, so furious at himself. He stared blankly at the floor wondering if he could ever defeat his panic, his disobedient body, his autism. He began to stim on his sensory toys. They led him to escape.

"Hello, Autismland," he thought.

31

Absolutely Not Possible

"**M**om," Mark said later that evening after Anthony had gone to bed, "can you please look at these videos I took?"

His mother was relaxing on the sofa watching a home remodeling show. "What are they?" she asked, barely glancing his way.

"Just watch and tell me what you think." He handed her his phone and showed her the videos he had surreptitiously shot of Anthony touching the alphabet board and answering his questions. She watched them closely, several times. She could clearly see Anthony touching 'o,' 't' and then 'r,' 'y.' She seemed to be holding her breath. Finally, she spoke.

"I have to show Dad," she said. "Can you forward these to me?"

"Okay." Mark knew his father had no interest in being nagged and forced to see "magic and fakery." He would no doubt think Mark was in denial, that he wanted to be the big hero, to show him up. And he knew that the tension at home was bound to increase, but he was not going to drop it. The plane he was flying was about to U-turn back to Anthony's desert island.

The next evening, Mark's dad came to his bedroom while Mark was sitting at his desk doing homework. "Mom sent me those videos," he said, his sentences clipped. "You know it proves nothing, right? *You* hold the board. *You* move his hand. *You* tell him the answer before you start. Honestly Mark, what do you think this proves?"

"I don't think it proves anything," Mark responded defensively, and then added, "but I didn't hold his hand the *whole* time. Just the first letter. He finished it."

"It proves nothing." His father stood in the doorway, his large frame blocking out the hall light. "Ask him a question without giving him the answer first or maybe I ask him something and you don't know the answer."

"I don't think it's that simple, Dad. I think it's hard for him. I looked at Marina's tapes. Obviously, her students have varied abilities, like, maybe it's a process. You don't run a marathon the first time you run, you know."

"Not even remotely comparable. He either communicates independently or he doesn't. If he lacks that ability, maybe it's because he doesn't understand." He paused, muttering almost to himself. "My whole family has gone mad. Only the dog makes sense."

"I make sense, Dad," Gary retorted, emerging from his bedroom.

"You do make sense, Gary," his father responded with a grin. "Thank you for that." Then he turned to Mark. "Let me prove it once and for all," he said, grabbing the letter board. He exited the room and walked up to Anthony, who was lying on the sofa and stimming on the iPad. His father asked Anthony to sit up. Then he sat down next to him, radiating annoyed energy. He handed Anthony the letter board and demanded, "What is the prickly desert plant called?" Mark had followed his father into the family room. Gary was right behind him. He always knew when a drama was unfolding. Their mother wasn't home. She was having a rare girls' night out with friends, all of them mothers of autistic sons.

Anthony immediately panicked. His father's anger always upset him and his lack of faith in him upset him even more.

Anthony had never faced a test like this before. He was sure his dad wanted him to fail to get everyone off his back. Anthony's hand froze in utter confusion. It was practically a paralysis. There was no way his hand was going to obey. The tension was so high, his father so annoyed, and the drama unfolding held his fate in its hands. He tried to get his finger to move to the letters but his hand didn't properly receive the message. Instead, his non-thinking limbic system kicked in. Anthony jumped up, flapping intensely and twisting at the waist.

"You see? There you go," his father said, as if the case was now closed. (Ladies and gentlemen of the jury, I ask you, is this a person who can think?)

"There you go, what?" Mark cried. "I have never seen you so closed-minded!"

"Really? You know your brother. How come he's magically communicating overnight? How come no professionals detected this ability? How come no teacher did, no speech therapist, not Natasha, not Dr. Hagerty?"

"I don't know, Dad. Maybe they're as open-minded as you!" Mark stormed out of the room. Gary agreed with his dad and told him so. He then went to the kitchen and made himself some toast. His father, meanwhile, retreated to the television. And so, Anthony was left alone, flapping his hands, grieving inside, hating his life and mourning his fate. He loved his fun-loving but brainwashed father, and he stimmed, whirling away his pain.

32

The Crackpot

Over the next few weeks Anthony gave up hoping and returned to his low-expectation life. Mark had stopped his experiments. His father had made it clear to everyone that he was sick of the whole discussion. Everything was back to "normal," only Mark stayed out a bit more with his friends and Anthony had stopped his daydreams and returned to his inner world of stimming. He felt bored in his stims, twirling, shaking, staring, tensing, but what else could he do? It wasn't as if his body would let him tell his father the truth.

Anthony didn't know it, but his father had contacted Natasha while he was at work and asked her what she thought of Marina.

"I'm sure she's a very nice person," Natasha had responded, her voice dripping with sarcasm. When he asked her for any other impressions, she told him what he had expected to hear. She thought that, though plenty of families believed in Marina, "it's highly doubtful her claims have any truth to them. I'm sure there is subconscious manipulation going on, or worse," she said. Then she suddenly stopped. "You're not thinking of bringing Anthony to her?" she asked, alarmed.

"Me? Not a chance," Anthony's dad reassured her. "But the rest of the family seems to think it's a good idea."

Natasha laughed bitterly. "Well, if you do go, please don't be fooled. Anthony deserves better."

He ended the call. He felt even more certain that his instincts were correct. So certain, in fact, that he was ready to concede a visit to Marina for the sake of peace. His wife had been pestering him to just go once. What did he have to lose by trying? His relationship with Mark was tenser than he liked, and if he was honest with himself, Anthony was out of sorts too, triggered easily and moping. Natasha had confirmed that it would be a waste of time, but he figured it was kind of like taking the kids to the Santa Claus in the mall when they were small. It made everyone happy, it was fake and they outgrew it. Eventually the kids realized Santa's beard was a prop. If they went to Marina, he reasoned, it would be easier for him to see her tricks. Once they went, he could fight her crackpot notions more easily. Then they could move on. It wasn't surrender. He was declaring war in his own way.

"Okay, I'll do it," Anthony's father announced to his family at dinner. Mark was home early and joined them at the table.

"Do what?" his wife asked.

"I'm willing to go to the crackpot once." He laughed while saying it. Gary was disappointed. He liked being on his dad's side. Mark and his mother were surprised, but pleased. Anthony's heart sang inside, but he also felt afraid. Just once? Oh no, not again. Another prove-it-now test. But he decided it was better than nothing.

"Dad, maybe you shouldn't go," Mark suggested brightly, desperately hoping his dad would take the bait. He could tell how toxic his doubt was to Anthony.

"Nice try," his dad replied. "There needs to be at least one objective family member there to keep things rational." On cue, Anthony started laughing out loud. It sounded a bit like yelping and shouting to his family, but he was laughing at his father, the "objective, rational" one. After all, alone among those at the table, only Anthony really knew how much he understood, how real his potential to communicate was. His mom and older brother had some hope and some expectation of success. His dad had repressed his hope and had little expectation of success. Gary had his video games. They interested him more than his brother's endless therapies.

"Good joke, Dad," Mark said.

"Pure coincidence," his father replied. But he looked embarrassed.

33

The Big Day

When the big day arrived, Anthony's parents picked him up from school early. They talked while they drove. "Keep your expectations low," his father cautioned.

"Keep an open mind," his mom replied. They drove on silently.

Marina's office was unpretentious. Two chairs faced a rectangular table that hugged the back wall. To reduce distractions, the room was devoid of artwork and table decorations. Additional seats a few feet behind the table allowed his parents to observe the lesson. Marina's attitude was friendly but no nonsense.

"Welcome," she said, shaking their hands. She was a slightly heavyset, middle-aged lady wearing a green top. She looked totally ordinary. Why did Anthony expect otherwise? "Hello, Anthony. Nice to meet you." She sat him at the table and pulled out her supplies: letter boards, a dry erase board and marker, a science book. She turned to his parents and offered a brief declaration. "I teach communication through learning." Then, she positioned herself to Anthony's right, and before he knew what was happening she had jumped right in.

Marina's first lesson was about the water cycle and she read to Anthony about the journey of water as gas, liquid and solid. Rapidly, she asked questions and demanded answers, directing him to first touch answers she wrote down as she talked that appeared before him as choices on the dry erase board, then quickly moving on to the letter boards. She refused to let Anthony escape the work. He jumped up from his seat and moved to the other side of the room, waving his arms and vocalizing, but she calmly brought him back, denying him an escape in stims, insisting he work to his capacity. Anthony felt exhilarated and angry. He returned to the table.

Let me stim, I want to stim! he thought, frustrated his reliable old escape tactics hadn't worked. He recognized what was happening. She was pulling the communication out of his reluctant body. She wasn't letting him escape into himself. She believed in him. It was still very primitive. His arm moved tightly and he had trouble scanning the entirety of the board, even a partial board, but her verbal prompts telling him to keep going, to keep looking, helped his hand to better obey his thoughts when it faltered, froze or hit a neighboring letter instead of his target. The urge to flee was overwhelming him, but she was utterly resistant to his manipulation. He felt simultaneously thrilled and urgently overloaded. *Can't you stop?* He grabbed her arm aggressively. She moved behind him, encouraging, persisting.

He worked on. She focused him on the task. Her pace denied him his stims. His beloved stims had been forced to retreat so he could answer: "ice," "steam," "water." "Solid," "gas," "liquid". What else might Anthony, the moronic flapper, know? She pulled answers out of him as if tugging a rope. Here was evidence of a mind that understood words, that understood the concepts in her lesson, that understood her questions. And she never once moved his arm.

Anthony had never worked so hard before. His mind toiled to get his eyes to lead his hand to the proper letter. Her constancy forced him to attend, to listen, to steer clear of Autismland. But it was so hard. He hated the hardness of communicating. Why was it so difficult? The isolation of an entire lifetime might finally be starting to recede a bit, but his mind clung to Autismland. *Don't go!* he told his familiar solitude. It was odd, hearing Marina verbalize the letters he pointed, letters that spelled words and made answers to questions. He was elated but he felt exposed, his private silence disrupted.

"Is water in gas form called steam or soup?" She placed the written choices in front of him on the dry erase board. What a nonsensical question! His hand replied, "steam," and she forged ahead. "Right, and water in gas form, also known as water vapor, evaporates. It rises and returns to earth in what form?" She again presented the dry erase board and wrote a different letter in each corner. "Which of these letters does the answer start with? He touched the R in its corner of the board. "Spell it," she instructed, switching to the letter boards again. "R-A-I-N," he pointed, with only one mis-hit, forcing the answers out, resisting her less, feeling for the first time his hand as his voice.

There was no time for emotion. Anthony was working too hard. His brain was forced to be present. He had to engage. There were no treats and no breaks, and to his joy, Marina talked to him like he was smart. She was calm, encouraging, composed. He realized that he trusted her. Tough though she might be, her instructions were purposeful. She understood him, respected his challenges, knew he could achieve. More, she expected him to achieve. That was new.

Today, Anthony thought, was like his birthday. Not the day he was actually born, of course, but the day he started to feel connected, to feel he had a stake in the game of life, the day he began to show a personhood that others could see.

"Excellent first session, Anthony," he heard Marina say.

He heard his parents move behind him.

His mother whispered, "Thank you." Her voice was trembling.

"How is this possible?" his father asked. His mother was kissing Anthony.

"These kids are so locked in," Marina said. "They must learn to move in a way that enables them to answer, starting with lessons, choices and spelling known answers and working gradually toward open communication, conversations and so on."

"How come he can do this but he got so many wrong on his flashcards?"

"I'm teaching him to move his hand the way he wants it to go, to be successful getting to the right letter. When he mis-fires I teach him to become accurate. I don't record it as an example of his ignorance."

His father shook his head. "I have to think about what I just saw." He kissed Anthony too and stroked his son's hair.

"Would you like to come next week?" Marina asked. His mom looked at his dad.

"Yes," they said together.

34

Change

The ride home was more relaxed than the ride there. Anthony's mother turned her head to look at him in the back seat. "I'm proud of you, Anthony. Good job today."

Anthony said nothing but he wished he could have said, *Thanks for bringing me. Thanks for persisting. Thanks for giving me the chance, Mom.*

The lesson had been taxing. Anthony was totally exhausted.

"I'm proud of you too, Anthony," his dad said after a pause.

Thanks, Dad, Anthony thought to himself. He knew his father was in turmoil inside. After all, he had seen with his own eyes that Anthony had the ability to answer questions without being manipulated tactilely. True, he started with choices and letter boards that did not contain all the letters of the alphabet, but he still chose correctly from a field of eight. It couldn't be random because his answers had consistently been on the correct letters, and it couldn't be due to a puppeteer's manipulation, because Marina's hand didn't move his.

She had explained how Anthony was still learning to use his arm to point purposefully to communicate, that he was still learning to look right and left, up and down, to scan an entire array of letters, to move his hand to the one he wanted with accuracy and reliability. She had explained that this took some time. Some students acquired the ability faster than others. But the goal was progress, learning and communication.

Anthony knew that all of this had turned his father's world upside down. His father was unusually quiet. It was obvious he was processing the experience. He was comparing what he had observed with what he had been taught to believe and he couldn't reconcile the discrepancy. He told himself that it was important to think about what Natasha had taught him; that is, the data had the answers. He had no reason to suspect Marina of fraud. Her hand never once touched Anthony, but maybe he picked up subtle hints of some sort. "No, that made no sense," he thought.

He knew that Anthony had been drilled and drilled on human expressions and emotions and not done well. Surely a kid who couldn't distinguish between a happy face and an angry face lacked the ability to read subtle cues. Perhaps he did better with letters than images? Maybe that was the key. He could not account for the difference between what he saw and the years of failed drills. He had no reason to think Anthony knew a thing about the water cycle before today. He had learned about it when Marina taught him. No, how was that possible? Anthony couldn't even add two-digit numbers. How was he supposed to process concepts like that? Anthony's father's mind went back and forth. He felt severely confused. He desperately felt like he needed to go for a walk.

Anthony's mother had been trying to hold in her feelings, but her voice trembled with emotion whenever she spoke. *She* was sure about what she saw. Her boy was smart. He understood language and he could spell. Her feelings were mixed; guilt, anger and joy filled her simultaneously. Her realization that an intact mind lived within Anthony filled her with elation. Her prayers would be answered. He could finally talk to her, tell her he loved her, and participate in conversations with her. Or at least one day he would be able to.

But her joy was tempered by guilt. How could she not have realized sooner? How could she have missed the signs? Her love hurt. How could a mother not have known? She punished herself mentally, thinking of the times she wondered but ignored her suspicions. She thought about the past with resentment, unsure whom to blame. But she also made a decision: She would not tolerate anyone telling her that this treatment was fake. "I don't think we should mention this to anyone," she said aloud, as much to herself as to her husband. "Please don't discuss this with Natasha or anyone at school. Not yet. It's too new." To her surprise, Anthony's dad agreed.

"That's reasonable," he replied. "I think this is something we figure out for ourselves. If it progresses, then it may be time to share what we're doing. If it doesn't, I don't want to hear Natasha saying, 'I told you so.'"

"Deal," his wife said.

From the backseat, Anthony listened and rejoiced. He liked knowing that his parents would let him learn without the experts hovering over him, making him anxious, refusing to see what was in front of their noses. His new skill was precious, and vulnerable. The last thing he needed was for the so-called-experts to nullify his efforts.

He felt happy and horribly sad. It was hard, harder than he'd expected. Marina was intense and no pushover. He knew she had been successful with other kids and she approached her job with confidence. He liked her. She believed in him. He had never been taught by someone who treated him like he had normal intelligence. He liked that change. His therapists always used to say how smart he was, but he never understood why they said that since they treated him like he wasn't. Marina didn't play that praise game. She just taught him in the way he needed so he could communicate his thoughts. He felt elated that he might at last find his voice.

He didn't want to feel sadness, but creeping up on his happiness, there it was. He thought about his lifelong dream of being able to talk. Now he was being given a chance to talk in a new way. That's what he had wanted so achingly. He should feel thrilled. But rejoicing over a few words that didn't even amount to a conversation? The force of his whole lonely life came crashing down on him. Look at Mark and Gary. They were so lucky. They took their luck for granted. Why was it him? Why not them?

And it was strange to be so locked in and suddenly compelled to answer questions. He felt exposed in a peculiar way. He had gotten accustomed to his prison, his solitary cell. He didn't like it but he knew it. He was like an animal, caged all its life, who had been taken to some grassy refuge, and was afraid to leave the cage. What was out there? The first steps were so tentative. Anthony had so little self-confidence, a lifetime of 'neutral no' and corrections on his every move. He wanted to be able to embrace this opportunity with all his heart. But he held himself back from hoping too much out of fear and years of squelched dreams. He had to close his eyes, he was so exhausted.

"Look, he's asleep," his mom remarked. The rest of the drive home was quiet.

35

Two Teachers

The week moved slowly for Anthony. His only thought was how he would do the next time he saw Marina and how she would push him to emerge from his shell. His low-functioning autism class felt like a sensory deprivation study. He learned nothing and sat waiting for the time to pass. He escaped mentally, visualizing dancing letters and seeing sound in colors in his synesthetic brain. It was good to make his own mental movie to drown out his teacher, Miss Harris.

No offense to Miss Harris. She was so kindly, so earnest and tried so hard to teach her students, but her expectations were low and her lessons lacked any content for Anthony. It upset him that, to her, he was just a big teenaged baby, ungainly, clumsy and odd, who still needed these insipid lessons. He admired her, though, because he thought she was lovely to look at and she obviously cared deeply. He hoped that his admiration of her energy and beauty would be enough to get him through her otherwise boring class, but it wasn't. When he misbehaved in front of her, he felt mortified.

He wished he could get a less attractive teacher next year, wished that he could actually learn in school, wished that he could stand up and leave, go home and stim. His hipster aide, Bradley, was bored too, but he tried to keep Anthony in his seat and he never lost his cool, even when Anthony refused to listen. Miss Harris flirted with Bradley often, but unlike Anthony, he seemed indifferent to her loveliness.

Miss Harris babied the teenagers in her class as if they were still in elementary school. She taught according to their limitations because that was how she had been taught to teach them. If she went a day without someone melting down, it was a good day. She tried to keep her class lively. But it's hard to make boring lively.

Marina was not young like Miss Harris, and she was not lovely for him to look at. She wasn't bubbly, cheery or patronizing. She didn't use rewards or tokens because she believed the learning itself was the reward. But neither was she boring. In fact, she was relentless. She expected Anthony to learn and to produce the way any normal kid would learn and produce.

After only one lesson with Marina, Anthony already knew that the way she taught him was the polar opposite of how Miss Harris taught. In truth, different from how anyone he had ever worked with taught. Marina was totally respectful, but also a taskmaster and a mom on a mission to help autistic kids in the same way she had helped her own daughter twenty years earlier. Her daughter's skills could not be refuted. Though severely autistic she typed alone on a keyboard, had gone to college and earned a degree in math.

Thanks to Marina, Anthony felt possibility for the first time ever. He had become so accustomed to feeling like an automaton, or as Anthony reimagined it, an *autism*-maton, that anticipating something was a pleasant change. He had so little faith in himself after so many years of fudging things up in his drills and in day-to-day life that he hardly dared imagine that he would triumph with Marina.

Because Marina was so different from anyone Anthony had ever worked with before, he didn't know how to react. He knew she knew he was smart. He knew she was impervious to his oppositional antics, that she had no pity for his protests, and that she wasn't going to give up on him. He also knew that Dr. Hagerty would never praise her, except perhaps as his model of an unethical charlatan. But she had done something new for Anthony. She had taught him an interesting science lesson (he hungered for science lessons), and helped him take beginner's steps towards a means of communication. He looked forward to more. Hope filled him to his eyebrows, and yet he feared himself. He knew he had a history of being a quitter, a protester, a giver-upper. The demands she made on him to pay attention, to persevere, to try, to force his body somehow to obey him, to sit and not flee, to sit and not grab her, to pull out the communication that lay within him was the highest, hardest hurdle he had ever had a real chance of clearing.

Anthony daydreamed of Miss Harris' loveliness, but he dreamed of Marina's lessons.

36

Brains On The Outside

Anthony had been seeing Marina for five months, and making steady progress. He now used a full letter board to answer her questions in complete sentences. He was just starting to use a keyboard, hard as it was, and to converse on normal topics. His skills were "emerging," as Marina told his parents. "He is learning rapidly. He will soon be transitioning to a keyboard."

Anthony loved Marina with his whole heart. Her face looked warm and kind to him now. She had a sparkle in her eyes. How had he missed that in the early days? Initially he had been so anxious, so overwhelmed by her pace, her demands, her faith in him, that he couldn't acknowledge her warmth. No, to him she had seemed like a drill sergeant, a martinet, Napoleon pacing and inspecting the troops with a scowl. He had had it all wrong.

Marina genuinely loved her students. She believed in them and she treated them with respect. Her theoretical approach was completely different from anything Anthony had experienced before. He constantly compared her to Natasha, to Hagerty. He remembered something interesting that Dr. Hagerty had said about autism in that old psychology magazine interview that Anthony had listened to so intently. It was remarkable how many of Hagerty's observations from that overheard conversation between his parents so long ago still stuck with him so tightly.

Dr. Hagerty had observed that autistic children looked like typical children physically, which he saw as a problem. They had two eyes and two legs, and hair and a nose and a mouth, he said. They *looked* like any other child, except for their brains. He had explained how their normal-appearing outsides were deceptive, how they fooled people into imagining a normal child lived trapped behind their normal looking faces and inside their normally shaped bodies; how they fooled people into thinking they had more potential than they in fact did. The true level of impairment would be obvious, Dr. Hagerty had told his interviewer, if only the brain impairment were visible, as obvious as a broken leg, as obvious as some other clearly visible cognitive pathologies were. Unfortunately, he said, the brain's symptoms in autism could only be revealed through behavior. Wouldn't it simplify things, he mused, if they could just see the neurological impairment as if through a window in the head, as if the brain pathology were visible on the outside of the child? Then parents couldn't delude themselves with false hope.

Now, as Anthony experienced the freedom of two-way conversation for the first time in his life, he wondered what Dr. Hagerty might think about Marina. He imagined the psychiatrist would not be pleased as he thought about all the deluded parents who were now convinced their kids were mentally intact, misled by wild claims and their children's normally proportioned faces.

No, Marina was definitely not Hagerty-approved.

For now, no one other than Anthony's family, Grandma, Robin and David knew that he was working with Marina. It was their little secret. The private meetings were a kind of joy for the family. Each week at first, and now twice a week, his parents got to know Anthony. They discovered that he was clever, interested and ready to learn, and to their delight they found out that he was funny and had a wry sense of humor.

Each day he felt his isolation melting away. At home, he had started typing with Mark and a little with his mom, still not fluidly, still rudimentarily, but from his point of view, and theirs, it was huge. Good-bye pictograms and high fives. His family, at long last, had started talking normally to Anthony. And what a relief that was.

37

Provoked

Marina had a strategy. Her goal was for Anthony to type on a keyboard or an iPad, to be fluent enough that he could express his thoughts, to go to regular classes if he desired, and to make himself a life. Gradually he got used to looking at an array of letters, surveying the whole field and touching the one he wanted. Initially, he needed big letters because his accuracy in aiming was messy. He sometimes hit near or next to the desired letter or perseverated, repeating the same patterns, in neurological loops, but Marina helped him break these patterns. His skill improved and the letters grew smaller, preparing him to type on a keyboard or tablet. He could now converse, write a message, even make a joke. Of course, according to Dr. Hagerty this was impossible. Jokes required theory of mind, the ability to think conceptually, and an ability to grasp puns. This defied the very definition of autism. Therefore, it could not be true.

Anthony typed better and better and faster and faster yet his speed was still snail-like compared to a person without his disability. He was still clumsy, his hands still inept and he still used only a single finger. But the transformation in his world was huge. He was happier. He was calmer and he wanted to do things instead of just stim. Stimming had become somewhat of a hobby now, not a life support system. Miss Harris had observed that Anthony was calmer in her class. It was true. He could tolerate it now, knowing that he had another life in Marina's office, knowing that together they were building an escape tunnel for him. Neither Miss Harris nor

Bradley, his aide, were aware of Anthony's secret, but they saw the results.

One day when Anthony's mom came to fetch him early for a dentist appointment, she met Bradley sitting with Anthony in the main office of the school waiting for her.

"Another good day today," he told her with a grin, stroking his goatee as he often did when he was trying to make a point. He was lean, pant cuffs rolled up and arms decorated from wrist to neck in colorful tattoos. "He's on a roll."

"I'm delighted to hear it," she replied, as if surprised.

"He's like a different kid," Bradley said, pleased. "Miss Harris and I have no idea why, but keep it up. Is he taking any new medication now that's calming him?"

"Nope, no changes." She smiled and left it at that.

Her answer wasn't technically correct though. Hope was a medication for Anthony's spirit. He could use tranquilizers, neuroleptics, anti-psychotics, whatever the array of drugs doctors prescribed for autism symptoms. But until hope could be packaged into medicine form, none gave him what communication did.

Anthony had also started an additional therapy after Marina mentioned that he needed exercise. Her vision was for Anthony to exercise both his brain *and* his body, to somehow build and strengthen their partnership. Anthony met with a personal trainer, Ben, to get in shape. It was quite different from occupational therapy, which he had stopped during his years of despair. His senses weren't being integrated. Instead, he was getting fit, so his body would be more coordinated, stronger and more flexible. He was losing his soft belly. The program was hard and Anthony at first resented being ordered to move, like any out of shape couch potato would. In his case, he had bigger reasons to complain. He was stiff, weak and had poor motor planning. It was hard. It hurt. It made him feel inept. And yet, bit-by-bit, his skills began to improve.

His new secret life had given Anthony goals that he felt might actually be attainable. He *could* get fitter. He *could* learn to communicate by one finger typing. He would likely never speak fluently, or play baseball, but he felt relief in getting better at something. He hoped to gain enough competence to force his doubters to believe in him. He often worried that that was unlikely.

Since Natasha had started her own agency, she had very little direct contact with Anthony anymore, though she remained indirectly involved in his life. It was her agency that provided Bradley as well as Bradley's clueless supervisor, Bette, who came to school on a regular basis to observe Bradley working with Anthony and to offer tips.

Bette had the supreme confidence of a person totally secure in her expertise. She was an autism specialist, or as she called herself, an "autism whisperer." *More like an autism waddler,* Anthony thought, looking at Bette's short, rotund frame. Bette observed Anthony and saw his stims, his mistakes and his oddness, and she lived to modify his stims, mistakes and oddness. For some reason, neither she, nor any of the professionals, reflected on why they were part of his behavioral patterns in the first place. Neurologically there were reasons why Anthony flapped, or bolted, or hopped around clumsily. Neurologically there were reasons why he flubbed his answers or picked up the wrong items following a direction. But to Bette they were just behaviors that needed correcting. Bette knew everything—without knowing anything. Her confidence was such that Anthony mentally mocked her each time he saw her. She enjoyed bossing Bradley and making modifications as she saw fit. She was consistently upbeat. And patronizing.

About a week after Bradley had told Anthony's mom how well he was doing, Bette walked into Miss Harris' class for her routine visit. Anthony was sitting at the table nearest the door with Bradley. "Hey bud, how are you?" Bette chirped, tickling Anthony's back. "High five." She put up her hand for a clap. Turning to Bradley, she inquired, "How has he been doing?"

"Better, calmer."

"How about academically? Any improvement?"

"He's not very interested," Bradley shrugged, "but he is more willing to cooperate."

"Hmmm," Bette pondered. "Any changes in his life?"

"Not that I'm aware of. You might ask his mom."

"He's lost some weight," Bette observed, patting Anthony's stomach as if he were a puppy. He imagined patting her copious belly in response. "Looking good, bud," she said, as Anthony began flapping his hands. "Quiet hands," she remarked, automatically. She turned back to Bradley. "He still flaps excessively," she said. "Have him hold something, or sit on his hands." Bradley said that he had noticed that the flapping was way down. This was the first time in days he'd even seen it. Bette looked skeptical. "Hands quiet, Anthony. Sit on hands. No hands." She was firm. "This behavior is stigmatizing," she told Bradley, as if that were big news. "You have to curb it immediately before he gets on a roll." Anthony sat on his hands, resentment filling him. "If he can get through one hour without flapping," Bette suggested, "give him a cookie. How about if we use the visual timer to let him know? We can put up a picture of a cookie. Time's up—bingo, a cookie."

"An hour seems pretty long," Bradley replied. Anthony had been doing well, and Bradley had a sense that this was going backwards.

"Okay," Bette shrugged, "make it less then. But he has to

earn his cookie pieces by not flapping."

As she spoke, Anthony got angrier. He jumped out of his seat and started heading for the classroom door in agitation. "I see elopement attempts continue to be a problem," she observed. She walked over to Anthony and pointed. "Sit on chair." For good measure she added, "All done."

Anthony was furious—more furious than he'd felt in a while. He wished he could scream curses at her. She was so stupid and arrogant. For his entire life, Anthony had been controlled by too many people like Bette. A dumb person made confident by her diploma, made confident by dictating to a helpless, silent child. Now that he had a place with Marina, a place where he could express his thoughts, his patience for the know-it-all attitude of someone so clueless and patronizing made him boil inside. Yet, she was too oblivious and too insensitive to recognize how he felt. His flapping was his body's outlet. Flap flap flap translated to, *Get the hell away from me, you dumb woman.*

Bette's response: "Hands down, Anthony. All done." Her entire approach was to look at behavior and to never see feelings.

"I'm very concerned about his behavior. This is unacceptable escalation," she commented to Bradley, as if Anthony didn't hear her.

Bette, of course, was the catalyst. She offended Anthony and enraged him and she lacked the insight to realize that her running commentary about him to Bradley and her baby talk to Anthony made him feel demeaned and angry. Bradley took Anthony outside the classroom where he paced in excited agitation, vocalizing and acting weird in public to the bemused interest of the neurotypical students who watched him. Bradley took him to the track and they walked briskly for half a mile, Anthony yelling out his frustration.

Bette followed and sat in the bleachers, observing and writing notes about him. She made note of how the regular students having PE stared at his inappropriate behavior, his nonsensical yells and wild hand flaps. Yes, as she told Bradley, these behaviors *had* to be reduced. In truth, this case frustrated her. Anthony never responded positively to her friendly efforts, to her behavioral conditioning. No cookies, or high fives or cheery back scratches made a difference.

If she were honest with herself she would have admitted that Anthony seemed to dislike her on a personal level. But how could that be? She was upbeat, *super* upbeat, and people with autism needed upbeat, big, broad, larger-than-life upbeatness. She didn't get it. She was an autism whisperer. Her clients loved her. But this kid refused to engage. Clearly, he was not a happy autistic.

Finally, Anthony and Bradley left the track and headed back to class. Anthony felt much calmer but when he caught sight of Bette scribbling notes about him in her binder his resentment stirred up immediately. She strolled over. "Hey bud, feeling better?" She gave Anthony a great big Bette smile, tickled his back and put out her hand for a high five. A battle raged inside him. He knew he had to stay calm, but every fiber in him longed to retaliate. He flapped his hands vigorously. Bette observed again, "These behaviors are inappropriate for his age. I'm going to develop a behavioral plan to reduce them."

Flap flap flap. *Go to hell, you stupid idiot!* Anthony shouted out of his flapping hands. *Stop interpreting me! Stop insulting me! Stop bugging me!* His flaps were his mode of nonverbal release, and Bette watched him, consternation washing over her face.

"I'm really concerned about these behaviors," she said, repeating herself. He seems to be regressing."

"He's actually been calmer recently," Bradley observed, a bit defensively. Bette was clearly dubious.

"It's important to be thorough with your data," she told him. "Notes should indicate each escalation, how often he aggresses. Note the triggers, if there are any, and the level of agitation." Bradley had to defer. Because Bette irritated Anthony every time she saw him, she assumed Anthony was usually edgy. It was hard for her to accept Bradley's, or even Miss Harris' denials when she saw for herself how consistently dysregulated his behavior was.

For his part, Bradley had observed that his supervisor seemed to have a magic touch that left Anthony in chaos—and Bradley dealing with the behavioral aftermath for hours after she left. But what could he say to Bette? It's you? Bradley wanted to keep his job so he always backed down. Bette waddled out, her binder held tightly, clutching its juicy observations close. If she were honest with herself, she didn't like Anthony either.

38

No, No, No

The weekly Bette visits always put Anthony into a funk of self-pity. That evening, he moped his way to the dinner table. It was pasta with his favorite meat sauce and salad, and this lifted his spirits somewhat. Gary came to the table in a funk too. He was unhappy at his high school, where he was now a freshman. He'd had a close group of friends throughout middle school but they had all gone to a different high school and Gary was having a hard time finding new friends. He responded by snapping impatiently whenever anyone tried to reach out to him and pierce his cranky mood.

Mark was home, too. He was practically a guest now at mealtimes. He had his job, his girlfriend, his studies, his own life. He often got home late and ate leftovers alone in front of the television or computer, joining the family meal only when his schedule permitted. But tonight, everyone sat down to eat together. Gary stared blankly, his headphones blaring music. Their father insisted he remove them. Gary rolled his eyes. They both raised their voices. It hurt Anthony's ears.

Thankfully, their dog, Dibby, created a diversion, barking sharply at the neighbor's dog across the fence. Gary went outside to get her. By the time he got back, the mood had cooled. As Gary and Dad traded ideas about how to get the two dogs to chill out, Anthony inhaled his food. He ate impulsively, intensely, wolfing it down, and when he was done he didn't want to linger. Tonight, he liked the dinner and he started reaching for a second helping. His mother seemed surprised. She was unusually slow tonight. In fact, she hadn't even taken her first bite. She seemed distracted. Anthony could tell she had something on her mind. Finally, she blurted it out.

"I've been thinking that maybe it's time to share how Anthony is doing with Natasha," she said. It was clear she had already decided. "Maybe we should invite her to observe a session." Anthony squeezed his leg tightly in distress. Today, after dealing with Bette, was not the day to hear this idea. He couldn't imagine Natasha having an open mind about it. Listening to his mother, he felt his stomach knot up. He thought of all his supervisions in front of Natasha and dreaded her opinions. His growing ability to communicate his thoughts by touching letters still felt new and vulnerable, and Natasha was judgmental. Her role as lead supervisor, and now head of her own agency, had made her even more accustomed to being obeyed, to being the final arbiter. She had the utmost faith in her methods and Anthony was not surprised to learn that she was no fan of Marina. He had overheard his father telling his mother about his conversation with Natasha—the sarcastic one, before Anthony's work with Marina had even started. Anthony didn't want her involved.

"Do you really think it's time?" his father asked. He'd been persuaded months ago by his wife to wait until Anthony's skills were further along and now he preferred to wait until Anthony was totally fluent. Then, hopefully, they could blow Natasha's socks off. He reflected on the things Natasha had told him about Marina when he sought her advice as an ally. Natasha was intelligent, no doubt, but would she be open? He knew it was only a matter of time before they had to tell her. Eventually she would have to know. But his gut said that now still might be premature.

"I think so," his mom replied. "Both Miss Harris and Bradley have noticed how good Anthony has been lately. They both asked me if I'd changed his meds. They should know what's going on so they can support his growth in communication and give him some academics—and obviously, Natasha will have to know if we want to explore mainstreaming."

Please, no, Mom, Anthony thought. Mark was looking at Anthony. He immediately perceived that his brother was uncomfortable. Mark had always been sensitive to Anthony's feelings. Even as a boy he alone believed his brother understood. His child eyes had been open and unclouded by theories. He had heard the theories, of course, but he observed that there was more to his brother than the theories allowed. His mom had seen the same glimmers of intelligence but they confused her because Anthony's purposeful behavior was so fleeting and inconsistent and he couldn't replicate it on demand, as the experts required. Mark figured those glimmers had to mean something. In his mind, the glimmers of intelligence and purposefulness could not be totally random even if they were inconsistent. Now, he felt vindicated by the changes in Anthony's life. It earned him his father's respect, his mother's gratitude, and he and Anthony had grown closer. He made a point of working on communication with Anthony once or twice a week, at least, for fifteen or twenty minutes, in relaxed conversation. Originally, they had discussed science, but now they sometimes just talked, Mark full of breeze and jokes, Anthony serious and poetic.

"Natasha has always been interested in helping Anthony succeed," his mom continued, sounding defensive. "This is part of his success, so I think she has to know. She's the director of his agency after all, and she needs to know eventually. I think she'll be open-minded." Mark wasn't buying it.

"You think she'll be open-minded?" he asked, glancing at his dad and loading his plate with pasta and sauce.

His father answered between bites, "I think Natasha is a skeptic, but she's reasonable. It's pretty hard to refute that he's communicating now, but she is pretty wedded to her beliefs." He vacillated, thinking of the things Natasha had said to him.

No, Dad, please, Anthony thought, panic filling him further. At least he could now convey his opinion. He just needed a little help getting started. Mark seemed to sense that.

"What do you think, Anthony?" he asked, shoving a letter board in front of him.

"No, no, no," he touched the letters firmly, over and over, in a sort of slow-motion loop.

Gary was slouching in his seat, his head resting in his hand, his elbow on the table. He rolled his eyes and made a snorting noise. He was nearly fourteen now and he'd shot up four inches over the past year. Gary didn't smile as much these days. Partly his age, partly his situation, and partly his nature. And he found pleasure in playing the antagonist at the family table. Sometimes he succeeded in starting an argument, diverting the attention from Mark and Anthony's spotlight to himself.

"What an unexpected answer," Gary said with sarcastic impatience, goading, the same kind of remark he'd made so often when he was a little boy. His feelings were much the same.

"Mind your own business," Mark snapped, glaring at his younger brother, exhibiting his usual annoyance with Gary's temperament.

Gary sounded petulant. He hardly cared what he was saying, but he knew his obnoxious remarks usually provoked a reaction, and that was satisfying. Negative attention was still attention and Gary had a lot of jealousy. Not for the autism, of course, but for his parents' time and energy that had disproportionately always gone to Anthony. And his jealousy had fermented over time into a kind of chronically peevish adolescent mood, especially now that the family was so thrilled about the letter board. In contrast, Mark's patience for Anthony had only grown, now that the two of them could communicate directly. The budding neuro-researcher in Mark was fascinated by Anthony's unique perceptions and point-of-view and Gary, who was just his ordinary, pesky little brother, often ended up on the receiving end of Mark's impatience.

"So what do you think then?" their mom went on, ignoring Mark and Gary's conversation as if it hadn't taken place. That was unusual. She normally got pulled into their dynamics, but this evening she was single-minded. She returned to her point about Natasha. "We have to do it some time."

"Let's give it a few weeks," his father replied. Over the past few months he had become more cautious. "It's very clear to *us* Anthony is touching the letters on his own but I don't want to risk any potential negativity now."

"I think you're being too cautious," his mom said, piling some more salad on her plate without seeming to notice that it was spilling onto the table. "Natasha isn't stupid," she added.

"She's definitely not stupid," his father agreed, "but she's an ideologue. Let Anthony progress a little more so that she can't deny it." His dad understood where Natasha was coming from. His own skepticism had gradually faded only because he finally stopped listening to reasons why it was impossible and allowed himself to see what truly was. Even so, Anthony's father still struggled internally with what he saw.

Years of believing that his son lacked the intellectual ability to understand language created a kind of cognitive dissonance for him. Now, he could see Anthony moving his own arm to a letter board and even typing on a keyboard that sat on a table and he watched Anthony give intelligent, coherent answers to questions. And yet… how could this be? One look at Anthony, who was still unable to tie his shoes or spread butter without ripping his bread or hang up his jacket properly, stirred up the old feelings. Anthony, who stimmed and wasted time by default, who had the impulse control of a three-year-old, was correctly answering questions about chemistry and algebra and writing poems that rhymed. Marina might say that the delays were examples of motor issues. Fine, but it *looked* like he thought like a very young child, like he was unaware, and *that* is what Natasha would focus on.

No, intuitively, he knew Natasha would not be able to see it. If it was hard for him, it would be unimaginably difficult for her. She would look for every reason to prove its impossibility, just as he had done, but she, he feared, would not allow herself to discard her theories and allow herself to see the fact that Anthony was typing his own thoughts. Natasha, he worried, would become an adversary, not a supporter. He tried to stall.

"I know where Natasha is coming from," he said slowly, carefully, trying to put an end to the back and forth. "You might be aware," he looked here at Mark," that I had my own struggles opening my mind to Anthony's communication. Natasha is like a professional skeptic. I was just an amateur." He sighed. "Her career is wrapped up in doubting this. I think we should take it slow to protect Anthony, and clearly that's what Anthony wants."

Anthony's mom disagreed. She was emotional about Anthony's communication and filled with a kind of proud zeal. It made her stubborn. She had overcome her own skepticism so profoundly that she wanted to change the world, and she felt guilty for not discovering Anthony's abilities sooner. She wanted to rush it, to fix things for him, to compensate. And she couldn't imagine an old associate like Natasha, who had known Anthony for most his life, had seen him grow up and seen him struggle so much, not being thrilled for him. And they needed Natasha. They needed her to help get Anthony a communication partner if he were ever to get out of the autism room. This made her push back at her husband.

"I think that it's impossible to deny his typing," she asserted. "And I'm proud of him. I want to show off this incredible thing he's doing. Natasha has known Anthony and us since he was two. She knows we're not irrational. She knows he's smart. I have more confidence that she'll be able to recognize his new skills." She always gave speeches when she was trying to convince people. She seemed to be trying to convince herself along with everyone else. Anthony recognized this mood in his mother. He knew she wasn't quite rational when she got on a tear like this. He reached for the letter board.

"He wants to say something," Mark said, prodding his brother once again. "What do you think?" he asked. Anthony was too upset for eloquence. He just needed to get his message across. He pointed forcefully to the letters again.

"No, no, no."

"Why not, Anthony?" Mark asked.

He pointed again, hitting the letters hard, "No!" He was having trouble expressing himself more completely.

"We got it," Mark said. "Why not?" Anthony struggled to answer. When he felt emotional his typing got internally garbled with raw feeling and it was hard to organize both his thoughts and his hand to type. He tried to collect himself. He got up and paced and had to be called back to the table repeatedly. At last, Anthony sat down again. He pointed to the letters, "Natasha does not…" Then he got stuck, his hand hanging in the air, wavering.

"Does not what?" Mark persisted. Of all the family members, he was the best at communicating with Anthony.

Anthony trusted Mark. "Natasha does not?" Mark prodded again, waiting for his brother to reply. Anthony sat there for what seemed like ten minutes, his face flat. Finally, he raised his arm and pointed.

"L-i-s-t-e-n," he wrote.

Mark vocalized the sounds as Anthony spelled them out. Then he summed it up. "Guys, Anthony says, 'Natasha doesn't listen.' He doesn't want her in on this yet." It seemed pretty obvious, but his mom was frustrated. She didn't want to concede. She started to argue but her husband cut her off.

"It's clear he wants us to hold off for now," he said gently. He was beginning to understand that his wife was waging her own battle—she wanted everyone to see what she saw, to believe in and to recognize Anthony. But she couldn't do this without her son's permission. She was used to speaking for Anthony. She wanted to override him. But he had his own voice now. She had invited this voice into their lives and she couldn't ignore it, even when it disagreed with her. And his message was clear. He wasn't ready to be scrutinized yet. Reluctantly, she agreed. They would wait.

"You know she's going to have to find out eventually," his mom said. "We can't hide forever. I do believe she will pleasantly surprise you. I have confidence that she cares about Anthony and she will be able to see his progress for what it is."

Anthony listened to his mom and thought, *I wish I had your optimism, Mom*. He dreaded the thought of Natasha observing him as he worked with his beloved Marina. He planned to say no for a long time.

39

The Wall

"I need to get Anthony out of that autism class," his mom said to her husband a few weeks later while they were sitting in the backyard, relaxing. She had just finished watering. The sun was out. It felt good, the first warmish day after so many chilly ones. She absently threw a tennis ball for Dibby, who skidded back to her with the slobbery delivery. She threw the ball again and Dibby was back again. Anthony was outside too, pulling leaves off plants and poking his palm with the end of a stick. He too was enjoying the sensory pleasures of the garden.

"It's ridiculous," she went on. "He learns kindergarten math and he's bored to death. It isn't fair to keep him stuck there. It's just biding his time. I have to tell Natasha what's going on." Anthony was pulling petals off a drooping rose nearby and sniffing them in his hand. But he heard this comment and his relaxation time, his sensory communion with the garden, abruptly ended. His respite from worry was over.

Anthony felt his panic level rising because he knew what it meant, what he could not avoid forever: To get out of Miss Harris's class, he would have to be exposed to the scrutiny he dreaded. It was inevitable. There was no other pathway to general education than to prove to the powers that be in the IEP committee that he had the capacity to sit in a regular high school class and learn and perform at grade level.

To be fair, he understood why the school might have trouble with the idea of him jumping from remedial to regular high school work in one fell swoop. He knew he would have to prove himself. Unfortunately, he was a nervous performer and he feared that he would be on trial. He didn't just fear it. He knew it. Yes, he wanted out of Miss Harris' class. But he wanted out without having to perform before a panel of school district specialists, Natasha, and Bette. And he knew that wasn't possible. He got panicked just thinking about it, but it had to be.

Natasha and Bette controlled his school support system. They had to be on his side in front of the school representatives if he was to escape autism class. They would have to buy in for Bradley to be trained as Anthony's communication partner. Without that, there would be no regular classes. His mom had waited a few weeks since the last time she brought this up but she seemed unwilling to delay the inevitable any longer.

"I know Natasha will hear me out," his mom declared confidently. His dad didn't say anything to object this time. He knew his wife was completely determined and that they were unlikely to blow Natasha's socks off in any case. It had to be done. The Natasha Question had an answer. It was show time.

Later that evening, as Anthony lay curled on the couch next to her, his mom looked through dozens of videos that chronicled his progression working with Marina. She told him that maybe Natasha could just view the clips. Maybe that would satisfy her. Anthony's heart did flips of joy at the possibility. "I know it's nerve-wracking," she told her son, "but it's what we have to do."

The next day, when Anthony was at school, she picked up the phone. After all the Natasha talk, she decided to call Bette first because Bette worked directly with Anthony. She rationalized that Bette would be excited to understand why Anthony had been doing so well and that this would smooth her path to Natasha. But it was more than that. Now that it was crunch time, Anthony's mom preferred to start by contacting a person who didn't intimidate her, and that was Bette. His mom often felt lower-ranking around Natasha. She left a message on Bette's voicemail hinting that she had some exciting news to share. A few hours later she heard back from Bette whose voice sounded curious and eager. But the instant Anthony's mom answered the call she doubted her decision. Too soon, she thought. She forced herself to press on.

"Hi Bette, I wanted to let you know what's new with Anthony," she said, trying to sound confident. She walked to her computer desk. She made all her important calls there.

"Oh, have there been any changes?" Bette asked keenly.

"Yes, a big one," his mom said, her stomach doing butterfly flips. "Anthony has been learning to type to communicate. He has been working for months with Marina Folvino. He types on his own. He's doing age appropriate work. He's doing amazing. He's ready to learn in regular classes, I think." The phone went silent for at least ten seconds. At first, his mom thought they'd been cut off. Finally, Bette spoke.

"Wow. I'm amazed to hear this. Why didn't you tell me sooner?" Her 'wow' sounded totally flat. At her last visit to school Anthony seemed to her to have regressed behaviorally. It was starting to make sense. He had to be under terrible stress working with that Folvino, and now his mom wanted him to do regular high school work! That, she was convinced, would only add to his problem behaviors. Anthony's mom explained that they wanted to let his skills develop for a while before letting everyone know about it. Bette listened politely.

"How did you find her?" she asked. "I've heard many mixed reports about her work."

"We were referred by a friend. Marina has been great for Anthony," his mom said. "He is blossoming." Bette thought again about her school observations. Her impression had been that Anthony was stressed out and angrier than usual. His mother had always been pleasant to work with and seemed a reasonable lady, but maybe the stress of seeing Anthony's stagnation and low functioning in life had finally driven her to seek magical promises. Bette remarked that she had observed that Anthony had been less cooperative in school recently. Did she think he was stressed out from seeing Marina? No, his mom didn't think so.

"Her methods are controversial," Bette said, and with that word, Anthony's mother's fantasy of a warm reception, of being supported, of securing Bette's help to butter up Natasha vanished. "Really, there have been many concerns raised about facilitated communication," Bette continued. "I think it's important to point out that often the child is being manipulated by the facilitator. In fact, there's no evidence that this method is successful or scientific. Double blind tests have proven that if the facilitator didn't know the answer, the autistic person couldn't answer correctly. You are aware of those tests, right?"

"Yes, I'm aware," Anthony's mother answered. She was now on the defensive. "I'm not calling to discuss the efficacy of FC or the tests, or even if what he is doing can be called a form of FC, since it's a different method. I'm just letting you know how well he is doing so he can receive an appropriate education."

"Is he typing all alone with no one with him?" Bette prodded.

"Of course not." She felt like she was flailing.

"Then he's not typing independently," Bette went on, sounding eager to persuade. "Miss Harris' class seems a good match for him. He is getting vocational experience and trips in the community. But he struggles with self-control, even in that setting..." Bette trailed off, then asked incredulously, remembering the beginning of the conversation, "You're not actually thinking of mainstreaming, are you?"

"Well, actually I was," Anthony's mom replied. Silence.

"That's interesting. I'm happy to discuss it with Natasha," Bette said, sounding clipped now. "I'm sure she'll have some suggestions."

Anthony's mom was trembling. She felt nauseated. She sat frozen, holding the phone. After a few moments, she hung up.

"Well, that didn't go well," she said aloud to no one. She sat looking around the room, realizing that Bette would not be on her side. She felt lonely suddenly and horribly anxious. And Natasha, oh my God, Bette was going to tell Natasha first! She would bias Natasha from the get-go. She would say that Anthony was messing up in school. She would blame it on Marina. His mom had to reach Natasha first, though it would not make a difference, she knew. She dialed in a panic.

"Hello, you have reached the voicemail of Natasha Olsen. Please leave a message after the beep, including your phone number, and I will return your call within 24 hours."

"Hello, Natasha," Anthony's mother said, trying to sound calm and authoritative. "Could you please call me as soon as you can? It's important." She felt like crying. The team that had supported Anthony for years, that she had hoped would be her allies, she realized, were likely to not be supportive. At best, she hoped they would politely disagree. But after talking to Bette she feared it could get very uncomfortable. She prayed she would intercept Bette. She knew she would not. But Natasha, she thought hopefully, is more intelligent than Bette. Maybe she will hear us out. Oh, why couldn't she just reverse time and delete that conversation with Bette? She prepared herself for what she feared would come.

An hour later her phone rang. Anthony's mom hadn't told her husband yet that she had called Bette first, and she knew he would be irritated. He would be right, she thought. Now Natasha was on the line. She braced herself and answered.

"I spoke to Bette," Natasha said, getting right down to it. "I hear Anthony is working with Marina Folvino."

"Yes, it's been wonderful for him," Anthony's mom said. She tried to build her case, talking quickly, telling Natasha of his growth. She again sat at her computer desk where she felt more professional. It didn't help.

"I'm interested in seeing him," Natasha said. "May I come observe a session? I hope Marina won't mind."

"I think it should be okay," Anthony's mom answered, feeling guilty for what her son would have to endure, what he had been so nervous to do. Marina wouldn't mind. Her goal was outreach. But Anthony would. She hadn't listened to him tell her how he felt and she had done what she wanted anyway. She was upset with herself. Throughout the conversation, Natasha never criticized Marina. Natasha had the sophistication not to antagonize Anthony's mother and the diplomacy to build her case later. Natasha would observe and then later gently point out all the proofs of how Anthony was being coached and manipulated. That was Natasha's plan, anyway. Anthony's mom got off the phone thinking that Natasha was more open to learning than Bette had been and that made her feel hopeful again. Observing a session would be powerful and should persuade her. Maybe it wouldn't be so bad.

40

Skeptical

The next day, Anthony's mom hand-delivered a thumb drive to Natasha's office so she could review the videos. She still hoped to spare Anthony the in-person scrutiny. Natasha was in a meeting, so Anthony's mom left it there for her. Later that day, Natasha sat on her ergonomic chair in her office and looked through them methodically. In many of the videos Marina held his letter board. She sometimes had her hand on his shoulder. She sat by his side the entire time. And she constantly prompted him to keep going and look at the letters.

Natasha did what Anthony's dad had done: She searched for Marina's cues, anything that would somehow direct Anthony to the letters. It was hard to see where the cues occurred, but it was also hard to say how much he did on his own. True, he moved his own arm, and true, the letter board stayed stationary, but he only communicated this way with Marina. His skill was not generalized to others. The proficiency was dependent on Marina being there by his side and because she was questioning him she was obviously familiar with the material. Wasn't this proof enough that she was manipulating him somehow? It was hard to see *how* she did it, but Anthony needed Marina by his side. That much seemed clear. Get her out of the room. Let him type on his own, alone, or let him type equally fluently with everyone. Until he did that, Natasha would remain unconvinced.

But even for Natasha, her theory that Marina was manipulating Anthony didn't add up. According to Natasha's own copious data, Anthony had no ability to read subtle cues. He couldn't understand human behavior, emotions and facial expressions, so how was he supposed to be skilled at such an advanced level in picking up these signals? After all, Natasha herself lacked the ability to see how Marina was manipulating him.

Well, autistic people sometimes have savant skills, she thought. Perhaps he was gifted in this area. She remembered how her staff had to stare straight ahead during his discrete trials because he had been acutely responsive to their slightest glance and would pick up the card they glanced at, skewing their data. On the other hand, Anthony had never indicated any potential to communicate at a higher level or recognize subtle emotions in all the years of drills, so it must be that this picking up cues was an isolated savant skill he possessed that somehow had never been tapped into before. What else could it be?

Natasha had seen Dr. Hagerty a few months earlier at the university. They had even talked about Marina and other practitioners like her. Hagerty was furious, pacing back and forth in his office, his desk and shelves scattered with stacks of scholarly autism research. "These people are dangerous!" he shouted. "They make claims that they can get low-functioning children to communicate fluently and go to high school in honors classes, yet somehow these kids can only communicate through these few people. They have no means to communicate with anyone *but* these people. This tells you all you need to know about their 'methods.'" He made quotation marks in the air around the word. He was on a rant. "It's like the folly of crowds, a kind of delusion, if you will. I pity the parents who surrender their reasoning to follow these claims, particularly those who have been involved in ABA. They have had the benefit of data driven programs to reveal their children's potential for learning language, and it's hands off. It is all the child's capacity." He raised his voice as Natasha, and a few of his graduate students, sat in his office listening to the expert. "They move, prod, motor and manipulate. It alarms me that this absurd phenomenon is invading autism treatment!" He stepped outside the office building to smoke and Natasha and the graduate students followed him out. "I am determined to expose this hoax," he muttered as he strode into the corner of the courtyard.

Natasha had never seen Dr. Hagerty lose his cool before. It left her shaken. Now she had to face this on a personal level with Anthony. She had known Anthony for almost fourteen years. She had always been able to work well with his family and they had been cooperative with supervision suggestions. What changed for them? Why did they decide to go this route after so many years?

It was essential that Natasha observe Marina in person. She reasoned that more of her clients would be making the same requests in the future and she would need to be familiar with what was going on. Natasha made time in her busy calendar to go. She inquired if Bette could come as well but Anthony's mother said she preferred if only one person came at a time. After their phone conversation, his mother really did not want Bette there—ever.

41

Observation

On the day of the observation, Natasha, tall, lean and impeccably groomed, shook Marina's hand. She stood nearly a head taller than Marina, whose motherly appearance seemed almost shabby in comparison. Marina greeted Natasha politely, then seated her in an unobtrusive corner of the room and proceeded to work with Anthony at her long table next to the wall. Marina began her session with a history lesson on hieroglyphics and cuneiform and she used a letter board. Immediately Natasha's radar went off. Marina had her left index finger on Anthony's shoulder. Was she giving him subtle cues this way? Natasha looked carefully to see if Marina pushed or moved her finger, guiding him somehow to touch specific letters, but no, Marina's finger just rested lightly on his shoulder.

Natasha interrupted the lesson. "May I ask why your finger is on his shoulder?"

Marina paused briefly. "It gives him a sense of his body," she replied. "It gives him a grounded feeling." Natasha found this puzzling, but kept quiet. "Maybe Anthony can tell you," Marina went on. Anthony felt nervous telling Natasha anything, but Marina encouraged him.

"My body," he started to point, "is floating. This keeps me on land." Natasha watched, shocked. He had touched most of the letters clearly. Sometimes he dragged his finger across the board sloppily, but other letters were right on target. She could see it herself. How had it been accomplished? Marina moved her hand to the middle of Anthony's back, resting the same finger lightly in one spot. She asked him about the history lesson but Anthony wasn't finished. He slowly answered, "Body boundaries."

"Oh, so you want to talk more about this now," Marina chuckled. "Okay." As Anthony pointed to letters, she removed her hand altogether. He continued, with no difference in the results.

"My body is not my own." He touched the letters. Natasha watched. Sometimes he hit the wrong letters and Marina gave him feedback to touch the correct one. Maybe that was how it happened. It was like a symbiotic communication.

"Excuse me," she asked, as if Anthony had not communicated his message, "why do you hold the board for him?"

"Anthony is gradually learning to hold it himself," Marina said, accustomed to explaining, utterly un-defensive. "He is learning to transition to it but it is hard for him since it requires a lot of motor control. But he is using a keyboard or tablet on the tabletop. We'll show you later."

Natasha had no idea how this made sense. Surely Anthony had the ability to hold the letter board. It seemed to her that he had been made intentionally dependent on Marina. This alarmed her. She was eager to see him use a tablet on the table. As Marina held the board with her right hand, her left arm dangled by her side, not touching Anthony at all.

Using all his concentration, Anthony pointed on his board, relaying his message. "Natasha, I need to go to school and learn." Natasha didn't know how to respond. On the one hand, if she replied directly and conversed with Anthony she would be acknowledging that he had communicated with her, but she was unsure if the message had really originated with him. On the other hand, if she ignored it, his mother might be offended. She felt trapped in an ethical dilemma. Finally, she avoided doing either.

"Would it be possible for Anthony to tell me more on his tablet?" she asked. Marina set up the tablet on the table.

"This is slower for Anthony," she remarked. "The keys are smaller and it requires greater motor precision." Then she turned to Anthony and briskly asked him, "What do you want in school?"

He typed unassisted, "I want tp goto normakl classed." Marina let him continue without correction, even with his typos. Voice output spoke the words with the errors. "I want teepee go to normakel classed."

Natasha stared. Then she finally spoke. "Okay. Good job typing," she said. "Good job." It was the only way she knew how to address him. Anthony was tired and wanted to stop. He wondered if Natasha believed in him or not. He wondered if she would help him move to a typical class. He began to flap his hands slightly in excitement and fatigue. Out of old habit, Natasha redirected him immediately.

"Hands down," she said.

When the session ended, Natasha stayed behind to speak with Marina while Anthony and his mother headed out to the parking lot. He was anxious to unwind in the car.

"How much of this communication is he doing himself?" Natasha asked Marina.

"What do you mean?" Marina replied.

"How much is his own initiating? He's getting feedback through your touch and verbal prompts, isn't he?"

Marina looked at Natasha. "He is learning to control his body to express his ideas. It's a process that takes time to develop fully. He typed independently on the tablet. You can agree?"

Natasha took a moment. "He moved his own arm to spell

answers. You sat by his side the whole time."

"How would that tell him what letters to touch?" Marina asked.

"He is not fully independent, in that case," Natasha answered.

"No, he is learning a new skill. It's a process," Marina repeated.

"But what would you call it then?" Natasha pressed.

"I'd call it communication."

"Oh, of course." Natasha was trying to maintain a respectful tone. "It's just he seems to require your presence in order to do it."

"That's correct. I'm teaching him."

"And why did you touch his shoulder and back?"

"Most of my clients get no touch. However as Anthony explained, he has issues with proprioception and it seems to give him body awareness input, but that guidance has faded quickly and most of the time there's no touch at all, as you saw."

"I imagine that doing that could potentially prompt him to touch certain letters," Natasha mused.

"How do you think he gets messages of which letters to touch through a stationary finger on his shoulder or his back?" Marina asked Natasha. "If you hold someone's hand when you talk, does that mean they are prompting your communicating?"

Natasha laughed. "I can talk with anyone. He can't. There's a big difference."

"Yes Natasha, but you don't have autism. And *that's* a big difference."

Natasha left the room and headed to the parking lot. She found Anthony's mother standing outside waiting for her. She saw Anthony sitting in their car listening to music.

"What did you think?" Anthony's mom asked Natasha enthusiastically. She was proud of Anthony's performance.

"Wow, it was illuminating. She's a very interesting woman. Anthony tries so hard to please her. He worked really hard. It's fascinating." Natasha tried to answer without saying anything committal.

"He is communicating at last," his mother said, her own enthusiasm making her miss Natasha's ambivalence. But Anthony heard it loud and clear. He was unsurprised. "I appreciate you coming," his mom continued, smiling broadly at Natasha. "Now you see why we need to get him into a different class."

Natasha had more to say. But this wasn't the moment. "Thank you so much for inviting me," she finally answered. To Anthony in the car she called, "Good job, Anthony!" She gave him a fist bump through the open car window.

"I'll call you soon," she said to his mom before driving off.

42

The Assessment

Natasha called Bette on her way back to the office. "Do me a favor," she instructed. "Make a laminated alphabet board and bring it to school with you next time you see Anthony. I'm curious if he'll answer questions with you. Or better still, use a communication app with him on your iPad."

"Sure. Why? How was the observation?" Bette asked.

"Well, I'd like to see if the skill is generalized at all. To be honest, it looked fairly impressive in her office, but I have a hunch he won't be able to replicate it with anyone else, and you know what that means." She paused. "You have such a good rapport with him, it would be interesting to see how he does."

The following week when Bette visited the school to observe Anthony and Bradley's progress she brought a letter board and an iPad with an icon-based communication app on it that Anthony had never seen before. She placed it in front of him.

"Hi, bud," she said, and waited expectantly. He wasn't sure what she wanted him to do. "How are you?" she finally asked, cheerily. Anthony didn't move. He felt frozen, like he was glued internally. "Can you type hello?" she asked, getting a bit frustrated.

He sat, wishing she would just leave him alone. The app was too congested with icons, not letters. He wasn't used to it, he had a hard time seeing where things were positioned, and he had absolutely no trust in Bette. His body felt locked in a vise. Bette had no idea how to open his neurological pathways to communicate. He knew immediately that Natasha had sent her to gather data to prove his incompetence and he resented them both fiercely.

Biased buffoonery, he thought. *You can add that to your useless logbook.* She persisted.

"Hey, bud, I want you to type what this is." She held up a pencil.

Go away, you idiot, he thought. She waited a moment.

"Okay kiddo, let's try this," she suggested. She pulled out an alphabet board and put it flat on the table. Anthony had always had his letter board up at eye level. His visual focus wandered. He had trouble catching the letters that were in the wrong location and so far from his gaze. He didn't expect Bette to realize that. He got angry thinking about what she was doing to him. *She is such a moron,* he thought, *such a stupid idiot. Leave me the hell alone!*

"What are you doing?" Bradley asked.

"I'm working with Anthony on typing, but he isn't demonstrating the skill."

"How could he type?" Bradley asked, his mouth hanging open, too stunned to stroke his strip of beard. "He doesn't read."

"I know, right?" Bette said. Anthony hated her passionately in that moment. Bette turned to start discussing Anthony with Bradley. She lacked the courtesy to talk away from him and his classmates. To her it was like discussing a three-year-old using technical jargon. No biggie.

"Could you please step outside?" Miss Harris finally said. "The kids are getting distracted." They stepped outside the classroom. Hipster and butterball. Bette told Bradley that Anthony's parents believed he typed fluently. She said that she needed to verify if he truly had the skill or if it was solely due to facilitation. From what she understood, the facilitation had been quite invasive. He had been motored through everything, his hand moved for him from letter to letter. Bradley shook his head.

"I'm shocked," he said. "That seems totally unlike his parents."

Bette laughed. "Well, you know denial isn't just a river in Egypt. He's totally dependent on cues and hints from his partner and his parents now want him to be transferred to general ed."

"What?!" Bradley's mouth dropped open.

"I know, right?" Bette laughed at his reaction. "So, our job," she went on, "is to keep him in the proper placement. Can you imagine how the school district would look at our agency if we advocated for a kid like Anthony to go to general education classes?"

"Wow," Bradley said. "I had no idea." They reentered the classroom. In their absence, Miss Harris had been sitting next to Anthony trying to engage him. He looked at the big smile plastered across Bette's face and dreaded what would come next. Bette stood near him.

"Hey, bud," she said, sugar sweet, "I was just telling Bradley how good you were doing typing. You're so smart." She tickled his back. "Can you tell me what color this is?" she held up a blue pencil case. Anthony sat paralyzed. He had no confidence in this woman. She didn't think he could communicate. It was obviously a test to prove his failure, not his success. The letter board was still flat on the desk, not in his comfortable visual range. Everything was wrong. She had no understanding of his neurological challenges. Inside, he was cursing at her.

Finally, Bette sighed deeply and said, "Okay, I've seen what I need." Miss Harris was watching.

"What are you doing?" she inquired.

"Just assessing Anthony's typing ability, or lack thereof," Bette replied.

"Oh, is he learning to type? That's so cool. I saw that documentary last week about it. I was hoping to learn more." Miss Harris was gazing at Anthony with an intrigued look on her face.

"Seriously? I think it's a hoax," Bette said, as if Anthony were invisible.

"Maybe," Miss Harris said, "but it looked like several of the kids were totally independent. I mean, how incredible if we have the means to help them express themselves!" Anthony, for the first time since Bette arrived, breathed with relief. Miss Harris was an ally! He felt hope once more.

"May I try?" she asked.

"It isn't necessary," Bette said. "He doesn't respond at all. Most likely all his responses come straight from his facilitator. At least that's my impression." Bette stepped out of the room to call her office. Miss Harris, disregarding Bette's comments, sat down next to Anthony and as she had observed in the documentary, held up the letter board at eye level. He felt a surge of relief with Bette out of the room. Miss Harris' calm energy felt like a key opening his internal locks. Before she even asked him a question, Anthony brought his index finger to the board.

"F-U-C-K B-E-T-T-E."

Bradley was watching. "What the hell?" he said. It wasn't perfect, but the message was clearly readable. Profanity often is.

"Did you see that?" Miss Harris said to Bradley. To Anthony she said, "I guess you're pretty mad." Just then, Bette reentered the room. She saw Miss Harris sitting by Anthony's side.

"Did he do anything?" she asked. Miss Harris felt embarrassed telling Bette what Anthony said.

"He did point with me a little," she said.

"Really?" Bette asked doubtfully. "Did you have to touch him or hold his arm?"

"No, I never touched him, though I held the board at eye level.

"That's facilitation," Bette said.

"I didn't touch him or manipulate the board. I just held it." As usual, Bradley said nothing. He always tried to avoid confrontation with Bette.

"What did he say then?" Bette asked derisively. Miss Harris blushed and she suddenly felt a need to protect Anthony.

"Um, he said he was mad."

"He wrote, 'I'm mad?'" Bette asked incredulously.

"No, actually he swore."

"He swore."

"Yes."

"What did he swear?"

"At you," she said quietly, looking down.

"How interesting this happened the moment I stepped away," Bette remarked. Bradley, meanwhile, had moved to the other side of the room, getting some supplies, trying not to get involved. He felt himself caught in a delicate situation, and as always, wanted to stay in Bette's good graces. Bette stood behind Anthony frowning in irritation and making him nervous.

"Can you get him to repeat it?" Bette demanded. "I'll try," Miss Harris said. She knew Bette thought she was being passive aggressive to her.

Anthony didn't know how he did it. His body usually froze when he felt anxious and Bette made him anxious, but Miss Harris was a comforting presence and he had something important to tell Bette. Lifting his arm, his index finger clearly pointed to the letters, "F-U-C." Bette flushed.

"I'm outta here," she announced before he could complete the message. She turned abruptly to leave.

Anthony had no idea if her anger was toward him or toward Miss Harris. He finally concluded it was both.

43

Five Phone Calls

Following Bette's visit a series of phone calls took place. The first conversation was between Bette and Natasha. Call Number One:

"I just left Anthony's class," Bette told Natasha as she walked to her car. "I brought my iPad and a laminated letter board. I tried to work with Anthony. I got nothing. He didn't even move."

"That's interesting," Natasha said. She was doing administrative work and turned away from her computer to concentrate on what Bette was telling her. She crossed her legs, one time too many, over the knee and back at the ankle, as she often did when thinking. She looked like a corkscrew.

"It's my impression he is not doing his communicating independently," Bette reported, fuming inside. "Every time I tried to engage him he failed to respond."

Natasha swiveled her chair back to her desk and watched the fireworks exploding on her computer's screensaver. She thought about what she had observed in Marina's office. "I noticed he was dependent on Marina coaching him or touching his back when I was there," she told Bette, sounding relieved that her impressions had been confirmed. "Clearly his skills aren't generalized to others. She's got to be influencing him somehow."

"I totally agree," Bette replied, "but the teacher, Miss Harris, claims he communicated with her when I stepped out of the room."

"Oh, I'm sure," Natasha laughed. "No doubt she was

moving his arm to the Ouija board."

"She alleges that he independently cursed me out."

"She what?" Natasha was paying attention now. "Why would she say that? Do you have a conflict with her?"

"No, absolutely not," Bette answered. "She's a naïve kid with her first class, but she seems okay. She watched that documentary about autistic people who are supposed to type and got convinced kids were communicating independently."

"I watched it," Natasha said. "It was persuasive. If I didn't know better, I'd have been convinced too. Marina was on it with her adult daughter and she really does seem to type on her own."

"Really? You think it's a savant splinter skill?"

"Either that or she's one in a million," Natasha said. "Or else misdiagnosed to begin with. Since the diagnosis includes language processing deficits, then obviously if she processes enough speech to function well in college, most likely she has a misdiagnosed expressive language disorder and motor disorganization. Still, people like her make it harder for us when it comes to the low functioning kids like Anthony."

Bette didn't mention the F-U-C she had seen with her own eyes. It just didn't compute for her. Surely it had to have been generated by Miss Harris. "So, where do we stand with him now?" she asked Natasha, opening her car door.

"Let's see if this blows over by itself. I don't intend to do anything differently with him. Whether they think he communicates or not is irrelevant as far as I'm concerned." Natasha had a lot to protect. She wasn't going to go down this road with Anthony so easily. "He has so many issues to address and he's in the right placement now. Can you imagine him keeping up with a general education class, or disrupting all the students with his vocalizations? If his parents approach me, I'd be compelled to clarify the services we can provide, which would be 'stay-put.'" Natasha again swiveled in her ergonomic chair. The fireworks screensaver exploded on her screen in red and pink. She was thinking about what to do. "I recommend you not discuss anything with his parents right now. Just have them contact me if they bring anything up." Bette agreed.

"This whole situation makes me so angry," Bette said. "I can only imagine how stressed out Anthony must be feeling with all this pressure from his parents and Marina."

"I know," Natasha said.

"And now this teacher who makes him swear at me." Bette sighed at the absurdity of it all. They said goodbye and hung up.

Call Number Two: At lunch time Miss Harris picked up the phone and dialed Anthony's mom. Unlike Bette's communication to Natasha, this was an unexpected call. Like every parent getting a call from school, Anthony's mother initially feared something was wrong. She was relieved when she heard Miss Harris say, "I heard Anthony is learning typing. That's amazing."

"Yes," his mother replied, surprised. She hadn't authorized anyone to share the news. "How did you hear? I was meaning to tell you soon."

"Well," she stammered, "Bette came by today with a letter board and iPad to try to communicate with Anthony." Anthony's mom gripped her chair. "I had a feeling you might want to know, if you didn't," Miss Harris continued.

"No, I didn't," she said, trying to sound collected. "What happened?"

"He didn't communicate with her."

"Of course not," Anthony's mom answered, sensing that

she could speak frankly. "She doesn't know the techniques at all." There was a pause. Miss Harris went on tentatively.

"She left the room and I tried, too. I hope you don't mind." Anthony's mother's head was spinning.

"Did he communicate with you?"

"I held the board up. Bette had it on the table, so maybe that helped."

"Did he say anything?" Anthony's mom asked again.

"Forgive my language," Miss Harris said slowly, "but he pointed, F-U-C-K Bette. Bradley was there too, but Bette had stepped outside. I told her what happened and he did it again but she got embarrassed and left." His mother paused, a rush of different emotions pouring through her. Then she burst out laughing. She wouldn't have minded saying that to Bette herself sometimes. She felt pleased that Anthony had stood up for himself.

"Way to go, Anthony. Did she believe it?" she sputtered out.

"I don't think so." Miss Harris laughed, too. Then she made a request. "I was hoping I could come observe a session with his instructor. I think it's incredible if there's a way to help these kids tell what they think, if they have more inside than they can show."

"I'll try to arrange something." Anthony's mom was delighted. "May I ask," she continued, even though she knew the answer, "was it your impression that this was a kind of test?"

"Yes," Miss Harris said, a hint of sadness in her voice. "I think so."

"And he didn't pass?"

"No, I think he didn't." There was another pause.

"Thank you for letting me know."

"Of course. I'm thrilled for Anthony if he is communicating. I've noticed he's calmed down a lot," Miss Harris shared. "It seems like he's happier."

Next came Call Number Three, which was far less calm. Immediately after hanging up with Miss Harris, Anthony's mother texted her husband and told him to call her as soon as possible. He was sitting at his desk, working on a computer code. It demanded all his concentration. He wanted to work about twenty more minutes. Then he could reward himself with lunch from his favorite Thai place. He looked at his text, "Call me as soon as you can!!!" His concentration was immediately blown to smithereens.

"Can you believe that Bette went to school today with an iPad and letter board to test Anthony's typing skills? Without our consent!" His wife was practically yelling in his ear. "She doesn't have a clue what she's doing. She believes it's a hoax. He couldn't perform and now she's got her 'proof' it's not legitimate. How dare Natasha do this without our permission!" He let her vent. She obviously needed to. He was also still a little annoyed that she'd told Bette and Natasha about Marina. He had anticipated problems but he refrained from saying, 'I told you so.' They would eventually have had to find out, he knew. Finally, he spoke.

"I thought you said Natasha seemed supportive after observing the session with Marina," he pointed out. His wife raged.

"I guess it was just a big act. After all these years, too. What a two-face! I'm really worried now. How can they work with him? I've lost trust in them."

"Let's approach this calmly," her husband coaxed her, using his rational style to try to tone down the energy. "I'll call Natasha and maybe you can contact Marina and see if she has experience with this sort of situation. Let's see if it was just Bette acting alone or if it was under Natasha's direction.

I don't want to assume yet."

"Okay, I'll try to calm down," Anthony's mom said. She was practically hyperventilating. "And then I'll call her."

"And I will too," he answered. They were a team. Their marriage had been through so much stress but they worked seamlessly together most of the time. Anthony's dad had to set his work aside. His concentration was shot anyway. He made Call Number Four. Somehow, he reached Natasha right away. The conversation was awkward. She answered all friendly and professional. He made some small talk with her, trying to start the conversation on a convivial tone. She never mentioned Marina. Finally, he couldn't delay the point anymore.

"Listen, Natasha, the reason I'm calling is because I hear Bette came to class today to assess Anthony's typing. Were you aware that she was going to do that?" He waited. Natasha seemed to be pondering whether to deny or to confess. Finally, she gave one of her highly polished neutral comments meant to disarm irate parents.

"I talked to Bette about Anthony and his work with Marina," Natasha answered. "We were eager to see if his impressive skills with Marina were generalized to others. Bette is very experienced with autistic kiddos and has a great relationship with Anthony so it seemed ideal to explore this at her next visit. Did Bette or Bradley contact you about it?" Her approach wasn't working.

"No," Anthony's dad said. "Were they supposed to?"

"I was just curious how you heard of it."

"We should have heard from you or Bette prior to the visit, Natasha, to get our consent for this kind of assessment." His voice was still calm but there was force behind it. "What was the purpose of it and why didn't you communicate beforehand?" He was starting to feel angry but he tried to keep it contained. What kind of game was this anyway?

"It was innocently done." Natasha tried to placate him. "Please don't assume there was a conspiracy of any sort. We are eager to help Anthony be successful."

"As are we all." Anthony's dad paused and cut to the chase. "Do you believe Anthony types his own thoughts?" he asked.

"That's not relevant to our services," Natasha replied.

"How is it irrelevant whether one of your clients communicates or not?" he asked incredulously. Natasha was very uncomfortable. This was exactly the kind of situation she had hoped to avoid.

"Our contract is to help Anthony in his current placement, which is appropriate for him based on his current behavioral needs."

"What about his academic and intellectual needs?" Anthony's father pressed.

"Based on testing and performance, they are being met in Miss Harris' class right now. If he can only communicate with Marina, how would he be able to function in any other setting in school?" She was making herself clear. His skill was not generalized. Today merely confirmed that.

"Who said he can only communicate with Marina? He apparently doesn't communicate with Bette, but he is learning to communicate with others. He does it well with his older brother. It's a process. But more importantly, his skill is developing. It's miraculous to see it progress. You, of all people, should have an open mind. I understand skepticism. I was skeptical too, in the beginning, but this goes beyond skepticism. This is bias."

Natasha listened, totally flabbergasted by what she was hearing.

"I'm very sorry this happened," Anthony's father continued.

"I'm pretty concerned right now."

"We only want to do what's best for Anthony, to help him succeed at his optimal level, as he has been doing," Natasha responded.

"It looks like we see that level differently," he replied. He then demanded, "Don't let Bette, or Bradley, run any more 'tests' on Anthony unless we request it." Throughout the conversation, two very upset and angry people who saw the same situation completely differently struggled to sound calm and rational. Natasha was astonished at the level of denial she was hearing. She had not anticipated Anthony's father converting to irrational emotionalism. His wife, yes, but not him. Meanwhile, he was livid, and questioned whether Natasha had the ability to continue to provide his son with the proper support.

After Anthony's dad hung up, he replayed in his mind Natasha's comment that it was irrelevant to her whether Anthony communicated or not. What was the point of all her drills over all those years if language comprehension was irrelevant? He realized that it would be next to impossible to resolve their disagreement. No matter what Anthony did, Natasha would search for why it wasn't so. She had decided on the answer and now only sought to prove she was correct. They had worked together for so many years and they had always followed her advice. Now when they needed her to listen, she was dogmatic. He doubted whether Anthony could get the proper support from a team that misunderstood him so badly. The problem was that they were stuck in the middle of a school year and the wheels of change moved slowly. Somehow, they would need to carve out a truce with Natasha, at least until the end of the school year.

Call Number Five, between Marina and Anthony's mother, was more amicable. After hearing about what happened, Marina remarked to Anthony's mother that she wasn't surprised at all. For this conversation, Anthony's mother didn't need her computer desk. She allowed herself to sit in the recliner, drinking in the words.

"It is very hard for people steeped in theories and methodologies that concentrate on deficits and pathologies to identify signs of ability," Marina explained. Her calm approach was soothing. "Anthony's skills make no sense to Natasha because he functions poorly in many areas of his life. She can't understand how a young man who stims and can't take care of his basic needs can think and understand at a mature level. The discrepancy baffles her. She would equate it to an infant being able to type. She just can't see the potential." Anthony's mom was still incredulous.

"Yet she sat there and watched you!" she exclaimed.

"Yes, but all she looked for were reasons to disbelieve." Marina was bracing Anthony's mom for the truth and it was painful to hear. "If I touched his back then he was receiving tips telepathically. If I said, 'Go on,' but didn't touch him, I was giving covert signals.

"The problem," she continued, "is that, unless he sits alone in a room typing for an extended period, and imagine that happening given his distractibility and impulsivity, she wouldn't believe it, and maybe not even then. Then it would be memorized, or savant, or whatever they use to rationalize what they deem to be impossible. So, my advice is to keep on, let him finish the school year, get his communication skills better and better, more and more independent, use more tablet, and completely fade the back and shoulder touch. We'll need to find him a solid communication partner in school for next year and his skills will progress, making it harder for the Natashas of the world to deny."

"Thank you," Anthony's mom said. "Thank you so much."

"My pleasure. I've been down this road myself," Marina assured her. "Anthony will need to be prepared to prove himself. It's not fair, but it's the way it is. People are naturally skeptical and curious. We hope for open minds, but it's so difficult for many people to accept, and there have been highly publicized cases in the past that were questionable. That's why we will work toward helping Anthony be as independent as he can be."

"Yes," his mother said, drinking in the words. Marina gave her such hope. Never once had Natasha's guidance given her warm comfort, only the vague feeling that Anthony's performance had yet again failed to be what it ought.

"But," Marina went on, "the skill doesn't develop overnight. The same people who understand that other skills develop slowly and require trained instruction, still expect fluent typing in all settings and with all people from day one. It's unreasonable, and for people who claim to understand autism, they don't seem to understand the nature of neurological instability nor the gradual process of skill development that typing requires. What observers like Natasha *should* be looking for," Marina continued, "is progression."

The words clarified the considerable challenges Anthony's mom would face advocating on his behalf, but they also gave her a direction. After so much anger and resentment, that clarity felt like a balm to her. She slipped her shoes off and took a deep breath. Marina was a blessing.

"They forget that my daughter had her own slow path to where she is now," Marina shared. "She didn't start out fluent. It took a lot of practice. Some people have more or less capacity, of course, and people progress at different rates for a variety of reasons. That's true for any skill, but my advice to you is to just keep on with what you're doing. Invite his teacher since she's an ally, and keep working on typing at home. Teach him academics at home too. You can borrow his brothers' textbooks."

They would never be able to convince everyone, Marina concluded, "so don't worry about it. Just do what you think is best for your son, like you always have." Anthony's mom relaxed even more deeply into her chair. It was the first peace she'd felt since she had spoken with Miss Harris earlier that day.

"Thanks," she said again. "You know, we did lots of weird interventions when he was young. They never questioned any of it. He could be getting mega-doses of whatever, and they never found fault with all the ridiculous things we did. I could have injected him with hummingbird nectar and they would have said, 'fine,' but teaching him to type to communicate—that's witchcraft. They attack this because it threatens their theory."

After she hung up, Anthony's mother thought about what they needed to do. They would need to be systematic, pragmatic and determined. Anthony had to get an education, no question, but for now, she realized, it wouldn't be at school. The process would be more difficult than she anticipated. They lacked support from Natasha and her agency. The school would need to be convinced that Anthony could sit and learn in general education and accept his communication modality. If Natasha was not on board, Bradley could not be trained, and the school district might be even less amenable to letting Anthony mainstream. It would take some time to prepare the building blocks.

She would take it upon herself to teach him, recruit Mark if he was willing, maybe even hire a tutor, and help Anthony learn. He needed to learn so much: how to format an essay, basic facts about history, civics, science and literature. He needed to listen to audio books. He had to catch up on math. He couldn't just transfer to general education. He needed to learn not only academics, but to sit for long periods of time quietly, to work hard at a table, to believe he could be a success in school, and he needed to become a more proficient typist. He would also need the right support system. Painfully, that would not be Natasha, Bette or even Bradley, but for now, at least until the end of the school year, until Anthony's mom could find a more in sync agency and could persuade the IEP committee, they were stuck together. They must pretend to get along somehow. "Don't rush it," she told herself. "Make it work, plan, organize and go around the obstacles."

At least now she knew that Natasha and Bette were obstacles.

44

The New Team

Anthony's new tutor was a graduate student in education. Her name was Amy. She had never met an autistic person before, at least not one who didn't speak, so she had no preconceived opinions about whether Anthony was real or fake. Marina gave her some lessons and Amy took to it instinctively. She met with Anthony twice a week. She developed lesson plans. They read high school history, science and literature. He learned how to listen to a book in its entirety, though sitting continued to be difficult for him. He enjoyed the plots and stories even though he simultaneously hungered to retreat to the comfort movies he had watched ten thousand times before. He knew his movies were infantile and boring, but they pacified him into a familiar lull. The literature was different. He had to listen and visualize the characters on their adventures and during their crises. He loved some books, dreaded others, but learned patience in tolerating long narratives, and eventually came to like it. His mom, dad, and audiobooks were his narrators. Amy brought questions and essay topics. He learned to write outlines and entire essays. He learned to focus.

Anthony loved math. Math spoke to him. It was sensible and he was good at it. Amy brought video lessons from the Internet, and again he had to listen, and work. His brain started to engage and he found that he was doing more in his everyday life. He felt like someone who had been sleepwalking and was finally waking up. He sometimes longed to retreat into sensory Autismland, where there were no demands and no effort, but he longed even more to participate in the world.

Anthony realized that his life was opening up. He was still deeply challenged by autism but he saw that even with it, he could be part of life too.

Amy helped build a bridge to a real education for Anthony. He understood that he had never been a true student. He had been babysat, or even warehoused, but he hadn't been taught new things. It had been pure monotony. He discovered that he enjoyed listening to interesting new lectures. He loved that Amy spoke normally to him. He loved not being in his Autismland sensory swirl so much. He felt like he was becoming himself. He thought a lot about it. He was a modern Pinocchio. *You are a real boy.* He laughed at his mental image of the good fairy making the wooden boy real. His parents, his brothers, his grandma, even Miss Harris, spoke normally to him now. This transformation reminded him that he was now really free from the baby talk and the baby expectations.

Each week, Anthony worked out with Ben who gave Anthony gifts of body awareness, better proprioception, more control and better mind / motor communication. He studied with Amy and learned to be a student. Every day he was thankful for them, and for Marina.

Miss Harris had changed too. Thankfully, she'd had a totally different response than Natasha did when she observed Anthony's working with Marina. She sat in the back of the room in astonishment. Natasha had looked for failure, prompts and proof of how Anthony couldn't be communicating his own thoughts. Miss Harris just looked. She saw how he responded to Marina, how he was fully into the lesson and attentive. She started to see a young man with a personality unfold before her and rather than be threatened by it, she was overcome. He responded to Marina's questions, did algebra, learned history, and answered the questions that Miss Harris' relayed to Marina.

"Please ask Anthony how it is for him in my class?" she asked.

Anthony answered on the iPad, "It's boring. I don't want to offend you."

She answered him directly, "No offense taken. Do you think the other kids understand like you do?" she pressed.

"Yes," he typed.

"What should I do?" she asked. Her voice was shaking.

"Teach us like we are intelligent," he typed.

Marina turned to find Miss Harris weeping into her hands, her face covered.

"No one taught me that this was possible. I'm sorry for boring you, Anthony," she blurted, "and for not challenging you enough."

Anthony suggested Miss Harris give them age-appropriate lessons in class and talk normally to her students. She promised she would try, but explained that she had to adhere to a mandated curriculum. "But I will do better," she promised him. "I'd love to learn to communicate with you too."

The conversation with the lovely Miss Harris filled Anthony with pride and joy. He had influenced his life for the better, through words, for the first time, now, at seventeen years old. *It's high time,* he thought. From that point on, Miss Harris' class was better. Bradley was a hopeless case. He watched Miss Harris talk respectfully to Anthony, teach all the kids some information, and try to communicate with Anthony on the letter board. But he seemed totally unaffected. His job was to help keep Anthony calm and under control, to complete his dull classwork, and that was it. Who said anything about typing? He knew how Bette felt about it and he had been told it was irrelevant to his job, so he ignored the whole situation.

Bette's visits were shorter. *Thank God,* Anthony thought.

She was not as strutting since the cursing incident. She never knew if it had been Anthony or Miss Harris who cursed at her, but one of them hated her, clearly. She mostly tried to avoid Miss Harris. Anthony found it funny, watching Bette try to act confident and indifferent when she was obviously the opposite. For once he felt he had some power over her. Just having Bette leave him alone was rewarding. There was less faux cheer, fewer "Hi bud" greetings, and more observing from the back of the room. She even stepped out of the room now to discuss Anthony, instead of doing it in front of him.

Though Anthony still hungered for an education in school, he could honestly say that his life was much better.

45

Goulash Revisited

Anthony's grandmother invited his whole family to eat out at the "goulash palace." She had moved to a retirement community for active seniors about an hour away, so it had been a few years since they had all eaten there together. For years, it was their favorite restaurant. But patterns changed. Everyone had gotten older, and without Grandma living nearby, the restaurant ritual had become a thing of the past.

When the waitress nodded at them to sit anywhere they liked, Anthony told himself not to get nervous about goulash. No one in his family knew why Anthony had rejected his meal that night years ago. In fact, only Anthony and, it turned out, one other person, remembered that night at all. For the others, it was one incident of many. For Anthony, it had become a symbol of internal traps.

Out of tradition, they chose their familiar old booth, Mark to Anthony's right side so he could take his brother's order on the letter board. The waitress came by and handed out menus, but Anthony didn't need one. He knew exactly what he wanted. For symbolic reasons, his own private joke, healing—whatever it was—he wanted pizza. How far he had come, he thought, because he knew he would get it. Mark put a letter board in front of him and asked his brother what he wanted.

"Not goulash," Anthony pointed.

"Not goulash," Mark read out loud. His grandma practically jumped out of her seat.

"I knew he was sick of goulash!" She clapped her hands.

She was laughing.

"What are you talking about, Mom?" Anthony's mother asked. His grandmother was still chuckling. Remember that dinner long ago, she told her daughter, when Anthony had pushed away his goulash with disdain?

Anthony's mother smiled and shrugged a "kind of" sort of shrug. She barely recalled it. Neither did his dad. Anthony thought it was funny that his triumphant act that evening had barely registered for them. For him, it had been a monumentally important though trivial event, one of many moments that had defined just how limiting life was without communication. It had worked—to land him in yet another rut of quasi-understanding. After that evening, his parents got in the habit of always ordering Anthony chicken nuggets and fries. His mom knew he liked that, and it was a nice, safe dinner that he never pushed away. And then they stopped coming here.

"No goulash. We promise," his mom said.

"No goulash. No way," his grandma affirmed. Anthony could have lived with chicken nuggets, but Mark respectfully asked to take his order, and he at last had the ability to tell him: Definitely pizza.

This time, *everyone* got what he or she wanted. Gary got a burrito. Mark, a burger. Mom, a chef's salad. Dad, grilled chicken. Grandma, fish tacos. And Anthony had the pleasure of getting pizza. It came eight years late, but he savored every morsel.

Each day, Anthony tried to let go of the past, a time when the only way he could really state his preferences was by snatching or grabbing in apparent impulsivity, a time when he felt so powerless.

"How's your pizza, Anthony?" Grandma asked.

On the letter board he pointed, "Excellent."

Gary, on the other hand, was sullen during the meal. He had transformed even more fiercely into a moody teenager and no one was quite sure how to handle it. He made himself invisible with his hair over his eyes—because he often felt invisible. No matter what Gary did, Anthony was still the attention magnet. That was a given, because Anthony had always needed so much supervision and so many therapies. And now it was the typing that drew everyone's attention. Gary was actually happy for his brother that he could communicate, he was just sick of it being the only thing anyone ever talked about. It sucked the oxygen away from him.

It had always been like this. When they were small, Gary became competent long before Anthony could do much of anything for himself. Gary could play alone and entertain himself while someone else had to motor Anthony through everything. Someone else helped Anthony get dressed. Someone else helped him play. Someone else brushed his teeth. Gary coped by showing off his superior skills. It made him feel better (and Anthony worse). Of course Gary was better at doing things. His brain functioned normally. He was better at doing everything, and he was praised for his accomplishments. Yet for years Gary watched Anthony—bigger and older—get so much more attention for being inept. When he was a child, he found this very unfair. Little Gary could pour his own cereal but Little Anthony spilled cereal all over the table and floor. Guess who got the attention? Anthony poured something once without spilling? He got a fanfare. Gary poured a hundred times without spilling—well, everyone expected that. Of course Gary could pour without spilling. All kids his age could do that. He knew he didn't deserve a fanfare for doing ordinary things and the resentment that built up in him over time really wasn't conscious or rational, but it became constant. And as Gary grew into a teenager, it grew into anger and bitterness. Resentment wound through his double helix, becoming part of his DNA.

Looking at Gary's sad mouth beneath his mask of hair, Anthony realized that he wasn't the only victim of autism in his family. He could see that it wasn't easy for anyone. But Mark somehow was intrigued by autism. The scientist in him was always trying to understand it. Gary had always had a harder time with it. He didn't find autism interesting the way Mark did. He found it burdensome. Anthony knew Gary suffered, but there wasn't much he could do about it except try to get better himself. He couldn't stop his symptoms. They drove him nuts too. He felt guilty for how he had often inadvertently, and occasionally intentionally, made life harder for his younger brother.

Gary tried to put on his headphones, but their dad immediately said to forget it. This was family time, so absolutely no headphones were allowed at the table. Grandma looked at her beloved youngest grandson hiding behind his hair and told him some old, corny jokes, trying to pull him out from under his armor. It was classic Grandma.

Gary didn't mean to, but he cracked a crooked-toothed smile. By the end of the meal, they were all smiling again.

46

Goals

The overriding goal of Anthony's life now was to get into general education classes. He desperately wanted to get a diploma, to prove to himself and everyone else that he could do it. He thought that getting a diploma would end the debate on his legitimacy, but he was naïve to imagine that. For Anthony, new struggles for acceptance were just beginning. By putting himself out in public, he invited scrutiny. He was not a fan of scrutiny. Natasha and Bette were professional scrutinizers, and they messed up their interpretations consistently. Good intentions, data collection confused with insight, overconfidence bordering on arrogance, and of course, ideological zealotry, made their scrutiny pure misery for Anthony. He hoped most people out there in the world would be less opinionated and less determined to prove themselves right all the time.

It was hardly a fair battle. Professionals who had no motor disability—who spoke, handwrote and moved with ease—had no compunctions about believing that they understood the inner worlds of people who were too trapped internally to challenge their assumptions. Then, when these horribly trapped people made a breakthrough, hoping for some respect and recognition, they had to face a bunch of hard-headed know-it-alls who insisted that they were marionettes.

It was terrifying for Anthony, because he knew he would encounter this attitude from the very people who claimed to be on his side. He reminded himself how professionals like Miss Harris, Ben, Amy and Marina all believed in him, that now his parents, Mark, Grandma, and even Gary, some of the time, spoke to him normally. He also thought about David, who was taking regular classes. To get the education he wanted, he knew he would have to face the inquisitors. Some, he would be able to convince. Others were hopeless cases. But if he wanted to get an education, he had to be ready to fight for it.

His typing was slowly but surely becoming irrefutable. He typed on a tablet using a voice output app. It sat on a table. It had word prediction, backspacing if he needed to correct a typo, and he did it alone. His partner prompted him to look, pay attention, keep going, but only a fool would claim it wasn't him. It was a slow process. It might take around three to twenty seconds between each letter he typed, long enough for someone like busy Dr. Hagerty to pooh-pooh the accomplishment, long enough for Natasha to look only at the "keep going" prompts, long enough for them to convince themselves that they were watching him being manipulated.

Anthony had once imagined that if he could communicate, his symptoms would recede. Unfortunately, autism was very persistent. He was better at completing tasks. His attention span was longer. He was more motivated. But autism still clung to him tightly. Yes, he was intelligent and typed intelligent messages, but he was still the ultimate oddball who lined up objects, compulsively stimmed and had little personal care competence. His intelligence was different than his self-control. His motor system continued to be akin to one who was partially paralyzed, yet ironically it constantly moved around without Anthony's blessings, doing its own weird thing.

He understood why people couldn't see his intelligence sometimes. Strangers assumed he was infantile intellectually, not just behaviorally. He couldn't help the way his body acted. His system was compelled by obsessions and compulsions and urges to gratify sensory needs, and to the observer he looked like a generally confused person. So yes, Anthony was disappointed that autism was still with him so intensely, but he was also relieved to be able to express himself, even in his limited way. He was too slow to participate in the dinner conversation, too alone too much of the time, but it was better. It was much better.

Better, though not normal.

Anthony was intrigued by how the so-called scientific thinkers, like William Hagerty and Natasha Olsen, could watch a person with a motor system like his and miss the plain-as-day motor issues. He thought the signs of the disconnect between his brain and body were pretty damned obvious but, apparently, for specialists like them, his motor issues were easily confused with ignorance. He guessed that the lives of Natasha, Dr. Hagerty and others like them had become one enormous effort to validate their beliefs. Though they claimed to speak for autism on behalf of scientific methodology, Anthony concluded that they—unscientifically—lacked inquiring minds and receptivity to new ideas. It was hard to crack that coconut.

The system seemed stacked against him. Anthony thought about what happened to David when he was first mainstreamed. Robin had needed to change his school because the administration of the first high school David attended seemed to resent his presence and as a result, harassed him. The administrator who had permitted David to attend changed her mind once she realized he was hardly a "normal" autistic; he was a "weird" autistic. But by then David was already enrolled. So, the administrators intimidated David, trying to pressure him back to autism class. They made him feel unwelcome every day, following him, taking notes on everything he did, provoking and stressing him, and suggesting to his teachers that he didn't belong there or do his own work. The school had an anti-bullying policy that required the students treat vulnerable people like David better than the administrators did.

In desperation, Robin home-schooled David, seeing no other option. But eventually she found a high school that had no problem dealing with her autistic son, and it was only eight miles further away. He liked it there and performed well academically. Most importantly, the new school allowed him to be weird *and* intelligent.

David was Anthony's role model. He paved the way for Anthony to follow.

47

Talk To Me!

When homework and sports commitments permitted, Mark sometimes observed Anthony as he worked with Marina. He was becoming very interested in the brain and planned to switch his major to biology and neuroscience. He observed how calm and unflappable Marina was and how her calmness put his brother at ease. Marina was work-oriented and efficient, but relaxed and supportive the entire time they talked together. She understood Anthony's emotions and he trusted her, especially when he froze or got stuck. Mark tried to copy this when he typed with his brother.

His mother, on the other hand, had too much emotion invested in communication. If she couldn't follow what Anthony was saying because he pointed carelessly or mistyped, she became flustered and overwhelmed. Her anxiety affected Anthony. The moment his mom tried to communicate with Anthony, he became anxious. Then he couldn't perform. His finger would tremble near the letter, hover unmoving over it, or make circuitous routes to get there. His mom would get frustrated, and he would give up. Their attempts were fraught with anxiety. The poor communication with his mother was developing into a pattern of blocked energy.

"Why won't he communicate with me?" she complained to Marina one day.

"You have to relax," Marina answered. "It's not life or death. Think about how you need to listen to a foreign language you're learning. You can't overthink. You just have to relax and you'll understand better."

"I wish it were that easy," his mom said. "He communicates with Amy, and you, and Mark and Miss Harris. I take it personally."

"Is it personal, Anthony?" Marina asked him.

"She is too tense," Anthony typed. The whole dynamic pained him but there was nothing he could do about it. "I love Mom but she makes me feel pressured."

Marina turned to Anthony's mom. "Can you try to relax first before typing? When he feels pressure it's much harder for him to perform."

His mother answered her son directly, "I'll try Anthony. It's just that I want to talk to you better so badly."

With his dad, none of this was an issue. Anthony's father talked normally to him now, but he didn't work on communicating with Anthony directly. His relationship with Anthony was built on physical activity, television-watching and games. He wasn't going to sit and try to type with Anthony when Mark was so much better at it. Besides, Gary needed help with homework and his dad had only so much time and energy. He enjoyed listening to Marina, Mark or Amy converse with Anthony, and he was elated that his son had a voice. But in truth, his relationship with Anthony was based on hanging out, not chatting or doing academics one-on-one, and that was fine for both of them. Gary and Grandma never tried either. It just wasn't a part of their relationship.

Mark was, by far, the most skilled in his family at talking to his brother. Instead of the surging stress that shut Anthony down when he tried to communicate with his mother, Anthony felt pure pleasure communicating with Mark. Anthony saw that the situation hurt his mom's feelings and that wasn't his intention. He loved her, but this wasn't about love. It was about his need to overcome the paralyzing anxiety that interfered with his motor planning and tied him up in panicky, neurological knots. He was comfortable with Mark because Mark wasn't worried about communicating with him. Mark was relaxed and Anthony drew from his energy, his calmness and his faith in him. It helped him to keep calm.

When his mother watched them typing, she felt Anthony had rejected her. She recognized that this was emotional thinking. Intellectually, she knew that it was her tense energy that made Anthony try to end their sessions quickly. Whenever she sat down with him in front of the board or tablet, he would try to leave immediately. When she insisted he at least try to answer her questions, he would mis-hit letters or linger over them without touching them. Then she would get irritated, because she knew he could do better. "Come on, Anthony, why do you always do this with me? Just touch the right letter already!" This tied him up even more. His finger hovered or danced next to the target letter. It was like his old ABA drills. His finger wouldn't listen and his mom inadvertently made it worse by reacting emotionally.

His mom tried nearly every day to force a communicative partnership. Each time was the same. Why wouldn't he just cooperate? This time, she was close to tears. She sat next to Anthony at the dining room table radiating a desperate sense of urgency that sensitive Anthony took in and responded to by shutting down.

"How will we ever do homework when you're in general education if you won't type with me?" Her urgent plea certainly didn't help Anthony feel relaxed working with her. Mark was planning to transfer to a four-year college the following year, so she had reason to worry, yet her anxiety consistently had the opposite effect on Anthony from what she wished. The more she panicked, the less he could trust her as a communication partner. "You'll just have me, okay?" she said, her voice rising. "Touch the letter, Anthony!"

It was the Hindenburg crashing in flames. Anthony was hitting every letter wrong, his motor system flipping out. Then Mark got home. He had stopped to grab an apple from the bowl on the kitchen counter and was taking a loud bite as he gave his mom an exaggerated raised eyebrow.

"Mom," he said, "you have got to lighten up."

"That's easy for you to say," she answered testily. "Do you have any idea how important it is for Anthony to communicate with me? We're trying to get him into gen ed. How will he succeed if he won't work with me?"

"Mom, you need to get a grip," Mark said. "You are freaking him out."

"I know, I know," she said. "The thing is I get so upset when he doesn't talk to me." Mark put his hand on her shoulder and gave it an affectionate shake.

"Be patient, Mom," he said. "And lighten up." Then he edged her aside and sat down with Anthony.

She disappeared into the kitchen but she kept her eye on Mark, who was relaxed and easy communicating with his brother. Anthony typed as well with him as with Amy and almost as well as Marina. They were talking about school.

"What's your favorite subject, Anthony?"

"I like math," Anthony typed, and the voice activation program sounded out his words. Mark sometimes joked about Anthony's robotic voice output that couldn't convey emotion at all and always over-emphasized the word, 'I' at the beginning of his sentence.

"Me too," Mark replied. "How do you like history?"

"I like it but I don't like writing essays," Anthony answered. Anthony's mom couldn't help herself. She came marching out of the kitchen, wiping her damp hands on her jeans.

"Let me try," she interjected, seating herself at Anthony's side and moving Mark away. Immediately, Anthony's hand froze, and then it skittered across the letters but didn't land.

"This isn't fair, Anthony. Why won't you talk to me?"

She insisted Mark sit with Anthony again and ask his brother.

Anthony wished he could describe for her his fragile neurological stability. He absorbed her anxiety like it was his own. Her anxiety interfered with her own ability to understand him. It interfered with her ability to relate to him, and it interfered with his ability to move properly. Finally, he answered, "Don't try so hard."

She laughed dryly. "Okay, easy for you to say."

Mark recommended to his mom that she not work with Anthony until she was in a relaxed state of mind. "You've got to get into the zone, Mom. Be in the moment."

"All right, all right, all right," she said, throwing her hands in the air. "I got the message. Unfortunately, guys, you got a high-strung mother, but Anthony, it is important to me and I will try. I love you both very much." She kissed her two oldest boys and went to hang out a bit with Gary in his room, if he would let her. She tried to reach out to him as much as possible.

"No wonder I'm not relaxed," she thought to herself. "I'm always trying to juggle everyone's needs all the time."

48

The IEP

The IEP date loomed nearer. There was high tension in Anthony's home. The way Anthony saw it, this school meeting basically held his fate in the balance.

The individualized educational program, or IEP, was the multi-disciplinary meeting in which a committee decided where Anthony belonged. His mom was preparing, poring over her videos and notes on the computer and getting familiar with precedent cases. She constantly talked and planned with Marina and Robin. She had begun the process of transferring Anthony to another autism agency that would be more open to his communicative needs and would provide him with his school aide the following school year. But that was next year. For now, Bette would still be at his IEP, representing the agency. This filled his mother with dread.

Anthony had seen a private educational psychologist who allowed him to be assessed using letter board and tablet. It was very open-minded of her. Most people his mother had contacted refused, saying they couldn't attempt an assessment of a person who communicated in his modality. The psychologist watched very carefully during testing to be sure it was Anthony alone who answered her questions and not Amy, who accompanied him. It took a long time to complete all her tests, but according to her data, Anthony had solidly cleared the low-intelligence range and had clearly entered the above-average range.

The results indicated that he was intellectually capable of receiving a regular education. Behaviorally, he was still autistic, with all its idiosyncrasies, compulsions and impulsive actions.

Just like David, Anthony was requesting an education as a weirdo, not a cured autistic, which Natasha and Dr. Hagerty would have preferred. But if he waited until he was behaviorally cured to get an education, it would never happen. Anthony passionately believed that he deserved his chance now. In order to get that opportunity, he would have to convince the whole committee.

When the day arrived, the group met in a nondescript meeting room at the high school. They sat on old, stained gray chairs around a large beige conference table. Educational posters hung on the beige walls, admonishing students to stay in school and not to take drugs. Anthony's parents were both present. They sat side by side, armed with the educational psychologist's report and a compilation of videos that showed Anthony typing with Marina, Amy and Mark. They hoped it would be enough. The head of the IEP committee was a school psychologist named Rose Norris. She wore bright pink lipstick, a floral chiffon top and orange pants. She had never met Anthony, but she had gone to workshops on autism and she was skeptical of the claims that low-functioning autistics had high intellectual abilities. In her opinion, this could turn into just another ugly IEP where parents made grandiose, outlandish requests that the school could not ethically accommodate or afford.

The other attendees were Bette, the school speech teacher, the school adaptive PE teacher, and Miss Harris. The Adaptive PE teacher and the speech therapist presented their reports first because they had to return to work. They read their evaluations and observations. They talked about how Anthony met, or failed to meet, his annual goals—he had trouble balancing on one foot, throwing a football, speaking, and so on—and then left to return to their work with other students.

Bette then read her agency's goals for Anthony and noted that he had fallen short of many of them. The goals were detailed and measurable, such as whether Anthony had managed to initiate a greeting 40% of the time with single prompts out of 10 trials. Next, Miss Harris read her report. His parents, sitting close to each other, squeezed hands under the table. Then they got their turn. Anthony's mother gave everyone a copy of the educational psychology evaluation recommending that Anthony be considered for general education. She read the summary out loud. Then she told Mrs. Norris that they had prepared a seven-minute compilation of videos for the IEP Committee that demonstrated how Anthony communicated and how he completed academic work. Following this introduction, Anthony's dad began to set up their computer, but Mrs. Norris abruptly cut him off. Watching the videos, she said, would take unnecessary time and complicate what was clearly a cut and dry situation.

"I don't think that will be necessary," she told him. "We have a great deal of information already to make our determination based on the reports and performance of IEP goals. Based on this, it seems Anthony is in the proper placement in Miss Harris' class." Anthony's father turned red.

"You have an educational psychology evaluation proving his intellectual and academic readiness for mainstreaming," he said, not even trying to hide his irritation.

"We must look at the other criteria too," Mrs. Norris replied coolly. She had experience dealing with contentious parents in IEPs. "While this evaluation is very interesting, it is at odds with prior school district testing. Anthony simply has not demonstrated sufficient readiness for general education inclusion by other standards. In fact, our testing reveals that he lacks mastery of the foundational skills necessary for a general education placement." Bette avoided eye contact with Anthony's parents throughout this exchange. She stared at her fingernails.

"How accurate can your tests be if he is unable to communicate with the tester?" his mother asked.

"It's an accurate reflection of his performance level without assistance," Mrs. Norris replied.

Mrs. Norris then launched into a lecture of sorts, explaining how psychologically damaging it was for a student with autism to be in a placement that was too demanding and that such placements were disruptive to the other students as well. When Mrs. Norris asked Bette her impressions, Bette concurred, remarking that she had seen this first hand with other students. Moreover, Anthony was already exhibiting new signs of regression. She was greatly concerned that his behaviors could escalate, especially in a typical class setting.

Anthony's father turned to look at Bette. "Why are you trying to interfere with him going into gen ed? Your agency won't even be with him next year."

"I'm not interfering," Bette replied defensively. "It's my obligation to speak up and make recommendations based on Anthony's abilities and not on controversial claims and wishful thinking." Bette was adamant now. She was no longer staring at her fingernails.

Anthony's mom and dad were both getting ready to respond angrily when the door burst open. "I'm so sorry I'm late," a woman with flaming red-hair said as she rushed in. "I'm Lori Dreyer from augmentative communication. I came from downtown. Traffic was terrible. I hope you got my message."

She looked at the tense faces and quickly realized she had walked into one of those IEP wars everyone dreads. It became clear fast that she had inadvertently become the arbiter.

Calmly, Mrs. Dreyer listened to everyone as they explained their concerns. She asked to see the educational assessment and the other reports. After reading through them briefly, she inquired about the videos. She then surprised everyone by telling Anthony's parents that, of course, she would be happy to watch the clips. Mrs. Norris was frowning. She had wanted to draw the meeting to a close, but she was no longer able to refuse.

They began to play their compilation of clips of Anthony typing, untouched, on an iPad, keyboard and letter board while communicating with Mark, Amy and Marina. Everyone watched as he slowly typed out answers to age-appropriate questions on academic subjects.

But like the tale of the blind men and the elephant, each of them came away with different perceptions of what the clips demonstrated. His parents felt proud and vindicated. Bette and Mrs. Norris were underwhelmed. And Mrs. Dreyer? No one was sure where she would land. An eternity seemed to pass before she spoke.

"Well, I'm sure I can speak for everyone here," she said. "That was most impressive. He displayed a good grasp of math, science, use of language, as well as a good use of both low and high tech augmentative devices."

Anthony's mother and father turned to face each other. Could this be real? They had been anticipating a miserable battle that would escalate to an appeal. They were suddenly both smiling. Bette and Mrs. Norris looked annoyed. Miss Harris saw an opportunity and jumped in.

"If it's okay, I'd like to invite Anthony to join us now," she suggested. Mrs. Dreyer agreed readily, as did Anthony's parents. Mrs. Norris had no choice but to concede. So Miss Harris called her classroom and asked the substitute to send

Anthony and Bradley over.

A few minutes of silence passed before the pair entered the room and pulled up two chairs. Miss Harris sat herself next to Anthony, who was wide-eyed with nerves. She calmed him. She softly told him to just focus on why he was there, to concentrate on typing and to tune out any distracting thoughts. He tried to forget Bette was there. He tried to put the significance of the meeting out of his mind. He tried his hardest.

"Why do you want to go to regular classes?" Miss Harris asked him.

Anthony flapped a little and fidgeted, but slowly typed, "My hope is to get a diploma." It took him more than five minutes to type, he was so anxious. He felt all eyes on him. Several times, Miss Harris had to remind him to pay attention and to not get up.

"Thank you, Anthony," she said after he finished. "May he go back to class now or do you have more questions?" Miss Harris asked. Mrs. Dreyer asked Anthony if he was nervous.

"Very," he typed.

"Thank you for coming," she said. "You may go back now."

"Well," she said to the group after Anthony left. "My recommendation is that this student begin to try his hand in a few general education classes with the use of his devices and with the support of a trained aide. He can ease in gradually, starting in perhaps two gen ed classes. He can still use Miss Harris' class as his base."

"Maybe an art class, but how would he do academic work?" Mrs. Norris asked skeptically. Mrs. Dreyer understood where she was coming from. Placing Anthony in a general education class required imagination.

"The way we saw in the videos, I imagine," she said. (She did have imagination). "The law is least restrictive environment."

"Yes, but I don't believe district policy supports this kind of communication," Mrs. Norris complained.

"And he is totally dependent on his communication partner," Bette added.

"That's a good point," Mrs. Norris said, nodding. "How do we even know what's appropriate for this kind of student? He has never demonstrated high functioning capacity in school previously."

"He is demonstrating it now!" Anthony's mother nearly shouted. The meeting was going in circles. Anthony's father chimed in next.

"What the hell is the problem?" he demanded. He was a patient man but he had reached his limit. "What do you have to lose? Even if you don't think he's intelligent enough to learn, what's the harm in letting him sit in a regular class? Maybe he'll surprise you and perform well, but who does he hurt by being exposed to age appropriate lessons?"

"That seems reasonable to me," Mrs. Dreyer concluded, hoping to wrap up. She was speaking directly to Mrs. Norris, whose face betrayed immense disappointment. "He may not be ready to sit in gen ed classes all day yet, but based on his psych eval and the videos, he evidences high cognitive capacity." But before she could steer the meeting to a close, Bette raised her voice again. Her parting role was to be the protector of autism truths, to speak up against this travesty.

"With all due respect," she interjected, "I think this placement could cause Anthony psychological harm." Anthony's mother couldn't contain herself. The full force of all her son's trapped lonely years bore down on her, the realization of what he was up against hit her hard. Angry tears pooled in her eyes.

"He's being harmed now, stagnating!" she exclaimed. Anthony's father snapped, too.

"With all due respect, Bette," he spoke slowly, as if he were speaking to a particularly dense child, "no one here cares what you think." Bette had nothing to lose. She spoke forcefully now. Her careful professionalism had deserted her.

"I think you're both in denial," she said. And that was the final straw. Anthony's mother stared at Bette until the room fell silent.

"Time for you to leave," she said, soft but steely. "And please tell Natasha I'll be requesting a replacement for you for the rest of the school year." And with that, Bette picked up her supplies and strutted out of the room.

It was an unfortunate way to end a long association, but without Bette there Mrs. Norris instantly became more cooperative. She seemed to feel less confident that she could impose her views. And so, it was agreed that Anthony would mainstream for math and history. He could add another class, if he did well, the second semester. He would graduate when he was in his twenties. His success and the IEPs that would follow would determine whether Anthony would continue to mainstream for just a few classes while remaining on the alternate curriculum or be eligible to attend school on a diploma track. He had Mrs. Dreyer to thank for watching the tapes and keeping an open mind. Bette and Mrs. Norris had tried their best to keep Anthony in his designated place. But somehow, fate, in the form of a harried augmentative communication specialist, had intervened.

49

Getting Ready To Be Included

Summer vacation was nearing its end. Mark was busy readying himself to move out and transfer to a four-year college about 200 miles from home. With his departure nearing, Gary seemed to become a little less withdrawn, as if the idea of emerging from Mark's shadow buoyed him a little. As for Anthony, he was both nervous and exuberant about the changes that would await him in the new school year. Anthony knew he would miss Mark, but his own life was moving forward too. He was no longer standing still while Mark moved on.

He had met his new aide and new supervisor. Their agency was very different from Natasha's. Even the names telegraphed their divergent perspectives. Natasha's was called *Little Stepping Stones for Autistic Children* commonly referred to as *Little Steps*. His new agency was called *Autism Learning Strategies*. It was wholly supportive of typing to communicate. In fact, Anthony's new aide, Jeff, had already worked with another boy who typed. As a result, he quickly stepped into his communicative partnership with Anthony.

Before the school year started, Anthony and his mom visited his new teachers in math and history. Miss Harris came along and she warmly introduced him and explained a bit about his background and communication skills. The history teacher was kind and said he looked forward to the opportunity to teach a nonconventional student. He told Anthony that his own parents were deaf and that his first language had been sign language, so he had no problem with a student who typed and pointed to letters to communicate. Anthony liked him immediately. He was quirky and casual, never wearing anything more formal than shorts and a t-shirt. His name was Mr. Thomas.

The math teacher, in contrast, was brittle and grumpy, and Anthony disliked her instantly. She seemed uncomfortable having an autistic student in her class and talked negatively about how crowded her room was and how difficult it would be to find room for both Anthony and his aide. Flanked by Miss Harris and Anthony's mom, the trio immediately marched over to complain to Anthony's guidance counselor, who said the teacher was nearly retired and kind of burnt out. There was another teacher who might be a better fit, though. With the counselor's help, Anthony's schedule was adjusted. He now had Miss Gonzalez. She was young and inexperienced, but definitely enthusiastic, and Anthony immediately felt more optimistic. She even spoke to him directly. He was starting to believe that school might work for him after all. He loved Miss Harris but he was looking forward to getting out of her room part of the day.

He even told her so when she asked him what he was most looking forward to in mainstreaming. She quipped that regular classes were sometimes boring too. "True," laughed Anthony's mom. "You heard Mark talk all last year about his biology teacher and how she nearly ruined his favorite subject for him."

"That's normal boring," Anthony typed, "not drill boring." They were relaxed now. Even his mom finally seemed to be breathing more easily.

"You might be the only student I know who's looking forward to boring lectures," Miss Harris teased. On the serious side she added, "I am so happy to see you get this opportunity."

The night before the first day of school, Anthony lay in bed unable to sleep. He was filled with anticipation and excitement about what would take place. He feared messing up. He felt self-conscious. He also felt proud of himself. Tomorrow would mark his first time sitting in a regular class learning regular stuff. Educational equity. A dream come true, thanks to Marina. Others had also helped create this opportunity for him, but it was Marina who taught his hand to be his voice. Anthony tossed and turned, hope and fear pulsating through him like alternating currents. After three hours, he finally drifted off to sleep.

The next morning, he woke up early. His stomach was doing excited flips, but he was looking forward to going to Mr. Thomas' class and then to Miss Gonzalez' room for a geometry lesson. He knew part of the day he would still be in Miss Harris' classroom, but twice every day he would be out of it. He would be exposed to information he didn't already know. What a concept. He got ready in a state of nervous anticipation.

After hustling her two youngest boys—both hulking teenagers now—into the car, their mother first drove Gary to his high school, which was closer to home. "Have a great day, honey," she told him as he exited the car. Gary started to walk away. Then, to Anthony's surprise, he turned back.

"Good luck, Anthony," he said, staring straight at his brother. "I know you'll do great in mainstreaming." Anthony smiled on the inside. It pleased and surprised him to hear Gary say something kind to him without being told to. He wished he could reciprocate and not just sit there.

Gary was looking forward to this year too. His parents had convinced him to try out for volleyball and he had made the team. Over summer practice, he had made friends with some of his teammates. As difficult as his younger brother had been for so many years, Anthony liked seeing him look happier. He and his mom watched Gary blend into the crowd, lanky and long-legged. Then they drove five miles further to Monroe High School. When Anthony's mom pulled the car into the side entrance, they saw Jeff waiting. His head was shaved, his frame solid and powerful, and he wore a big, friendly smile in greeting. It was nice not to see Bradley. Jeff actually seemed eager to be there. That was encouraging. Anthony didn't smile in greeting. His face hung flat as usual. But, as he had with Gary, he smiled on the inside.

Jeff walked up to the car and gave a warm hello to Anthony and his mom through the window. She smiled broadly too and then said to her son, "Okay, Anthony, have a fantastic day. I'm so proud of you." She reminded him to grab his backpack, which would soon contain, for the first time, textbooks, notebooks and expectation. For the first time, it would serve its intended purpose. She gave Anthony a quick kiss and then he was out of the car and walking through the school gate with Jeff.

50

The First Day Of School

Their first stop was Miss Harris' room, of course. This was still Anthony's homeroom, and that was okay. Familiar felt good. Miss Harris greeted Anthony and said happily, "Big day today. You'll do fantastic." He went to his seat a little twitchy with nerves, anticipating that something out of the ordinary might happen, for once. The bell rang and then something did happen: Anthony and Jeff got up. Anthony put on his backpack and they walked out the door. Everyone else stayed. It was really happening.

Anthony was tall and Jeff was even taller. Side by side, they strolled through a bustle of students. It was a bit overwhelming and Anthony flapped a little in the throng. Jeff took note. Starting at the end of class, they would plan to leave five minutes before the bell rang to avoid the crowd. It took four minutes for the pair to arrive at Building 2, where they climbed up one floor to Mr. Thomas' room. As they entered, Mr. Thomas pointed Anthony and Jeff to two seats near the front door where a quick getaway was possible, if necessary. He made no special fuss over Anthony. He acted like he was just another student. No big deal. It was incredible. Anthony was thrilled at the normalcy of it.

Mr. Thomas started the class immediately, setting the tone. This was to be a no-nonsense classroom. He handed out a syllabus. He went over behavior rules. This was new stuff for Anthony. He was excited to be included. Mr. Thomas talked for about fifteen minutes about projects and penalties for assignments turned in late. Then he turned suddenly to

Anthony, who had inadvertently let out a few groans and other noises, drawing some curious looks. "Your classmate Anthony would like to share a few words with you," he explained to the class. Anthony had requested this. He and his mom had arranged it at their meeting with Miss Harris and the teachers before the school year started. The other students needed to be comfortable with Anthony so Anthony could be comfortable with them. Jeff hurriedly took out Anthony's iPad from his backpack and opened it to the voice output app. Anthony had saved the message he'd written there. As the other students watched, intrigued, Anthony touched the "play" button. A computerized male voice began to speak.

"My name is Anthony and I have autism," it said. "What that means is that my mind and body don't work together consistently. Sometimes my body doesn't get the message that my brain sends. This is why I cannot speak and why I communicate through my iPad or by pointing to letters on a letter board. It also means I sometimes move funny or make noises or may have difficulty regulating myself. It does not mean I am not intelligent or cannot think or understand. I understand everything and think just fine so I ask you to please talk to me directly and speak normally. Please know that if I make noises or act unusually it is not meant to disturb. I look forward to a fun year. Thanks."

When the message finished, Anthony felt anxious. What else was new? He worried about how the students would respond. But to his surprise and relief, they just accepted it. Mr. Thomas said, "Thank you, Anthony," and resumed his lesson. On the first day, he taught an actual lesson. What a concept. The focus of the class was American history and Mr. Thomas launched right in with a lecture about the Founding Fathers' vision and the principles of the American Revolution. Anthony hung on to every word. He was so happy to be learning. In a sea of tired faces, Mr. Thomas had one student who thought this was the greatest lecture of all time.

Anthony and Jeff left Mr. Thomas' room five minutes early to avoid the mob of students and return to their home base in Miss Harris' class. After the elation of Mr. Thomas' class, Anthony felt depressed. As much as he adored Miss Harris, she still wasn't teaching real content. She was following the mandated lesson plan with a little extra thrown in. Miss Harris had agreed to let Anthony do his classwork from his mainstreaming classes in her room so he and Jeff moved to a table in the corner of the room. Jeff tried to read in a quiet voice to Anthony from a handout from Mr. Thomas' class about the philosophical ideas behind the concepts of natural rights, but Anthony's classmate Hugo began yelling so loudly they had to step outside and find a table where they could work. When they returned to Miss Harris' room a half hour later, Hugo was calmer, rocking in his seat and squeezing his sensory ball.

Next it was time for math class, in the bungalow near the gym. Miss Gonzalez looked frazzled, and it was only the first day. Jeff claimed two seats for them and within a few minutes 45 students had streamed in. Many were unmotivated. Anthony didn't know it yet, but this was a geometry class for kids who were having trouble with math. As Miss Gonzalez started to explain her syllabus and expectations, several students just kept talking. She seemed confused and flustered by their rudeness, as though she had missed the discipline seminar during her teacher training. The students picked up on her weakness and insecurity immediately. They smelled it on her, and it empowered them. When she was finished with her orientation, Jeff asked her if Anthony could share his message. She had forgotten. "Sure, sure," she said distractedly. Anthony again pushed play and the computerized voice read his words.

The students listened attentively for the first and only time in Miss Gonzalez' room that day. No one laughed or made fun of Anthony. He was too different to be teased and he had a partner who would never have permitted it anyway. After class ended it was lunchtime, when Jeff had his break. Anthony sat with his autistic peers under the supervision of a school district aide as he ate and passed the time. She treated them like babies and talked to them in simplified speech. They could sit or stand, wave their arms in the air, make noises, twist and shout, it made no difference to her, but they couldn't leave the vicinity of the table. Anthony ate lunch quickly and then, because he couldn't chat, walk around, draw, or leave, he passed the time the only way he could. He entered Autismland. So, lunchtime became an Autismland stim fest. When Jeff returned, he saw that Anthony looked tense and unhappy. After spending nearly his entire lunchtime in a self-stimulatory blur Anthony had fallen so deeply into his head that it took effort to pull him back out again. Before returning to the classroom Jeff took Anthony to the track to jog and walk to help him self-regulate. It became their regular ritual after lunch.

After walking, they returned to Miss Harris' room. There wasn't much to do there the first day of school, no homework yet, and her lesson was simplistic. She was energetically spelling out vocabulary words from a handout about farms. Novel words like, 'sheep,' 'field,' and 'chicken,' challenged the students… to stay awake. When Anthony and Jeff came in she announced, "Today we will add something new to our lesson." She then brought out a book about agriculture, which explained how humans learned to domesticate animals. She began to read it out loud. The book was probably written for fifth grade students. That was okay. It was still light years more gripping than infant books. The students were restless, not used to this kind of teaching, not sure how to listen, but she plowed on, speaking in normal English, reading from the text and explaining how the domestication of animals changed human history. It was not a brilliant first attempt at teaching this way, but it was a valiant fifteen minutes. Overall, Anthony had to say it was a pretty good first day of school. He went home full of hope and happiness.

51

Different Classrooms

Over the next few weeks, Anthony got used to the changes. He used his letter board to complete his in-class essays in Mr. Thomas' class. The iPad was much slower but he used it sometimes to participate in in-class discussions. Unfortunately, his contributions were usually completed minutes after the class had moved on to the next idea. Mr. Thomas rolled with it. He made it seem like the most normal thing in the world, and by doing so, he modeled for the students how to respectfully listen and interact with Anthony. In just a few weeks in his class, Anthony had joined in study groups. Once the kids realized how smart he was they wanted to work with him.

Miss Gonzalez meant well. Her heart was in the right place, and the math was easy for Anthony, but he struggled to concentrate because of all the disruptive kids near him. He and his mom went to the guidance counselor once again, with Miss Harris for support. But the counselor said Anthony was out of luck; the other classes were full. That was how Miss Gonzalez' room became Anthony's greatest mainstreaming challenge. He often felt that his young teacher was intimidated by some of her rowdiest students and this created a leadership void. Somehow, he and Jeff still managed to complete his math work in her room or in Miss Harris' room, and on the positive side, it gave Anthony some valuable practice at tuning out distractions.

Anthony enjoyed working with Jeff. He was usually positive and unruffled, and he had a good sense of the triggers that overwhelmed Anthony. He could preempt many tough moments just by paying attention to Anthony's moods and body language. Jeff was not bored like Bradley, probably because his job was more interesting. Bradley just had to make sure Anthony did the minimum, while Jeff made sure he did his maximum.

It was a big difference. And it wasn't always easy. Sometimes, Anthony felt overwhelmed. One day in math class, he had a panic attack and roughly grabbed Jeff, who whisked him out of the room. It happened so fast no one would have noticed—if Anthony hadn't been yelling, visibly struggling and pulling on Jeff's shirt. Jeff knew what to do and took it in stride. He brought Anthony to a quiet bench near the track, where they sat side by side until Anthony could regulate himself. When he finally regained his self-control, Anthony felt humiliated and ashamed, but Jeff shrugged it off and when they got back to the classroom, the students barely cared.

Each day was hard because Anthony had to operate on overloaded senses. There was noise in the class, in the halls, in the cafeteria, everywhere. There were visually overwhelming bombardments of moving people, colors and action. It took a lot of work to retain his equilibrium. But Anthony was moving in the chaotic flow, no longer isolated in his little room in the corner of campus all day. Despite a few instances when it became too much, he was handling it well. That was the key. He was improving and getting ready for more.

His autism classrooms had a measure of tolerance for students who made noises, had fits, jumped randomly, shrieked, banged things and all the other compulsions that might overwhelm them as they all tried to cope with massive sensory overload in school. In autism class, one could act autistic and the incentive to control impulses was low. In general education, Anthony had to behave much more calmly and exercise control. That took a lot of work. And he knew that even if the typical kids talked or disrupted, they disrupted within normal parameters.

When kids talked back to Miss Gonzalez, which was often, she would send them to the dean. It pained Anthony to see that so many of his classmates didn't value their education; that they wasted their chance to get one. One day, a kid told Miss Gonzalez to shut up when she confronted him about talking to his friend during class. When she ordered him to go to the dean, he swore at her in front of the entire classroom. The other students hooted. Anthony watched it all, astounded. It mortified him that no matter how his classmates acted, he would always be the "weirdest" one.

Monroe High seemed okay with Anthony being where he was, and who he was, unlike David's first high school, which had harassed him and tried to push him back into autism class. Perhaps Miss Harris, behind the scenes, had educated the staff, making them more accepting. Whatever it was, Anthony was grateful. He felt comfortable in his regular classes. And he was driven. He had a point to prove to himself and to the professional community. He pushed himself hard to complete all his in-class work and homework, even if he did much of it with Jeff as they sat outside or in a corner of Miss Harris' class.

Anthony's determination was paying unexpected dividends. Each day he felt less internally driven by his impulses and more externally motivated. Being able to communicate his ideas in class was a dream come true. People who have never been denied this treasure naturally take for granted that communication is always there. Not so for Anthony. Every time he answered a question in class, he had a feeling of triumph that made him hungry for more—and proud of how far he had come. He felt frustrated too, thinking of his lost years and imagining the life he would likely be having if he had never met Marina. It was easy to imagine that. He need only look around at his classmates in Miss Harris' room. None had learned to type.

He often felt them watching him as he worked on history or math homework with Jeff. He thought it must make them feel frustrated and sad, watching a friend escape from the silent prison while they were no closer to escape themselves. It made Anthony feel down, even guilty, though he knew he had done nothing wrong. He had known several of his classmates since his years in Mrs. Lester's class. Kenny, Carlos and Robert communicated no better now than they did in elementary school. Anthony wished he could help them. He felt guilty for his own luck.

Another friend of Anthony's, whom he had known since Mrs. Lester's class, had a simple device that he was supposed to use to communicate his basic needs, and nothing more. He stimmed on it mostly, pushing the same key thousands of times until he had worn a little indentation in it. Anthony knew Hugo was smart. He showed it in many ways, but none of those ways used words.

Anthony had apraxic speech limited to a few select words and a few inconsistent phrases, like "go for walk" or "orange juice." But he wasn't very intelligible and his output wasn't reliable. Hugo had even less speech. In fact, he had the most severe verbal apraxia imaginable. Naturally he got tons of speech therapy, but no one had ever thought to teach Hugo to touch letters to communicate. Miss Harris wanted to, but Hugo's mother refused to let her. His mother actually said in front of the class, "This might be okay for Anthony but it isn't for Hugo. I really don't know how much intelligence is there. I don't think he has the capacity." Her words infuriated Anthony.

I didn't have the capacity either until someone taught me, he thought to himself. He was typing with Jeff as Hugo's mom spoke, and quickly changed course, keying into his iPad, "Hugo is smart." Then he pushed the 'speak' button.

Hugo's mother listened and said dismissively, "Hugo can't do that," as if Anthony hadn't been communicating directly with her and telling her something important about her son.

He's never been taught! Anthony screamed inside. Hugo's mom was so unused to conversing with someone with autism that she turned to look at Miss Harris instead. "I really don't think Hugo is capable of more than he does already," she said again, as if Anthony were invisible.

"May I try with him in class?" Miss Harris asked.

"What good would it do?" his mother said.

"But it's all right with you?" Miss Harris asked again.

"You can try," she finally said, "but I think you'll be disappointed. Hugo's got the mind of a baby. He doesn't follow instructions. He can't understand what I tell him. What's the point of trying to teach him that?" Her words were extremely painful for Anthony to hear.

Hugo had been stimming at his desk. He looked slack-jawed, as he always did. But about twenty seconds after his mother's remarks he suddenly became agitated, jumped out of his seat and ran toward her aggressively. His aide intervened, stopping him before he could grab her. He steered Hugo outside for a calm-down time out. "That's exactly what I mean," his mother said to Miss Harris. "He gets excited too easily and for no reason. I think it's better for him if he doesn't get stressed by this." On second thought, she told Miss Harris, it would be better for Hugo to steer clear of the whole notion of typing.

Hearing her revoke her consent, Anthony felt heartbroken for Hugo. His mother had underestimated him and misinterpreted his behavior, causing him to lose his opportunity to learn. Anthony believed that Hugo reacted the way he did because he was upset. After all, his mother had said to everyone that he was stupid and couldn't learn to communicate. His autism made him move like a clumsy oaf and react slowly, so it was easy to think he had no intellectual capacity and no chance. Hugo heard it every day. They all did. Anthony recalled hearing Hugo's mom tell Mrs. Lester, back when they were in elementary school, that she must be being punished, having a child like this. When Anthony typed, he could feel Hugo's eyes on him and he hurt for Hugo. He hurt for all of them.

Once again Anthony was in two worlds where he didn't quite fit. He was the only autistic person who was nonspeaking in any of the regular classes on his campus. And he was the only nonspeaking person in his autism room who typed or could communicate his thoughts. He felt like a navigator in his school, alone in many ways. Thankfully, he knew that other autistic typers, like David, had been successfully included in general education programs in other schools. That helped give him strength. But it didn't make his daily challenges easier.

Miss Harris was greatly supportive. She functioned as a kind of ambassador for him, helping his teachers understand how autism affected Anthony's behavior, sensory system and motor system. They listened with the distracted interest they gave to anyone whose suggestions placed demands on their time. To them, Anthony was just one of many kids they taught who had challenges. Maybe his were unique, but many of his classmates had family problems, learning problems, depression, financial hardship and other challenges and they came to school reflecting that. Anthony realized he was fortunate to have a loving family and a comfortable home to sustain him through his other hurdles. He had plenty of bad luck, to be sure, but when he looked at Hugo, and the angriest kids in his mainstream math class, he realized that maybe he also had some good luck too.

52

Typing Bachelors

Time passed more quickly now. Anthony no longer felt like a guy staying in the same spot, year after boring year. He had movement in his life. He was learning in school. He was getting decent grades. Kids said hello to him. He sat in study groups instead of alone. He was happier than he had ever been. Time also helped him to learn to stay longer in his classes, to sit quietly, to organize his brain better.

For once Anthony had a goal in life; that is, a big long-term goal. He had had many trivial goals before—biting off lollipop heads, stealing his brother's French fries, irritating Lily, bolting from his lessons—but none could be characterized as goals in life. It had just been Anthony getting back at his frustrating world. His victories were those of a powerless little boy who couldn't express his ideas to anyone and so took obnoxious revenge on his "helpers." But Anthony had a real goal now. He intended to get good grades, be fully included in general education, graduate with a diploma, and somehow make his way in life. Anthony lived in two worlds always, an internal sensory one and his outer reality, but now he found himself more and more often a participant in the real world.

He was still deeply autistic. He had once had the fantasy that if he attended regular classes he would be like Peter, looking nearly normal, talking, and "passing" as a normal kid. But Anthony had finally realized he could be educated as himself. He worked only once a week with Marina now. She felt he had progressed exceptionally fast, and he knew that eventually he wouldn't need their lessons anymore. He also met with fellow typers in a social group she had helped organize. The group offered Anthony his first opportunity to talk to his fellow autistics. They all typed. They all expressed themselves on augmentative devices or letter boards. It was his first community of peers.

A stranger observing the group would see a bunch of teenagers who looked away from each other and moved in funny ways. They might assume these awkward teens had no smarts, but all the participants were either attending regular schools and learning with typical teenagers or were being homeschooled at grade level.

Anthony met monthly on Saturday afternoons with these friends in a big office conference room that was empty on weekends and belonged to the father of one of the group members. They came mostly with their mothers, though a few came with both parents, and occasionally a trained communication partner came as well. There were five regulars and a few boys who attended sporadically. Anthony loved going because for once he didn't feel alone on an island. Knowing that he was not the only one like himself brought him enormous relief. David went with Robin, and there were others too, but as usual in Autismland, there were no girls, except the mothers. The ratio of autism skewed heavily toward boys.

On one drizzly Saturday in December, the boys filed in to the conversation group. Boris made loud groaning noises, David paused to sniff all the mothers' heads and Anthony flapped his hands slightly in anticipation. Their parents hustled them to the long table. The non-flowing conversation got off to its typically bumpy start.

"Tom has something to say," his mother announced. Tom then asked the group via computerized voice output: "Do any of you like to go on rides?"

David's robot voice was next to emerge from his computer's tinny built-in speaker: "I am so happy to meet with all my friends today." He had begun typing before Tom asked his question and pushed 'speak' before anyone had a chance to answer.

Immediately four others went to work on their keyboards, working at their own pace. "It is good to see my friends here," Computer Logan weighed in. "I feel lonely at school."

Boris used a letter board so was relatively quick. His mother spoke his words. "I love roller coasters," she read.

Anthony typed slowly and paused several times, distracted. About six minutes had passed before Amy announced that he had a comment ready. He hit the 'speak' command. "I don't like rides at all." His answer hung there, reaching back for Tom's question without quite connecting. He pushed away his iPad. He preferred the letter board sometimes.

Because everyone typed or pointed at different speeds, it often seemed like multiple conversations took place at once. Today, some, like Anthony, chose to answer Tom's question about rides. Others focused on David's greeting or brought up unrelated ideas that were burning inside. Many of the boys hardly conversed with anyone all month long. They often saved up topics to bring up when they got together. It was organized chaos. Amy, Anthony's tutor, had accompanied him and his mother. She was at his side acting as Anthony's communication partner when a true exchange took shape.

"Rides are too overwhelming," David replied. Not everyone heard him, so Robin told him to push 'speak' again.

Boris pointed, "They make me feel thrill."

"Too many bright colors and noise," added Anthony.

No one wanted to talk about feeling lonely. The boys took

in Logan's comment but it required no response. They were all lonely boys and getting together once a month was the big treat of their social calendar. Their autism might emphasize different symptoms; one guy hyper, one guy snail slow, one guy overwhelmed by rides, another made alive by them. But they had too much in common with each other on the big things. None spoke orally and each had lived much of his life perceived as unintelligent and unable to understand the behavior of others, speech or the world around them. And all of them were now at long last able to communicate and to learn in school. They understood Logan's loneliness and pain. Each one faced it every day, but they had come to this group for relief. Anthony chose to talk about rides rather than heartache. He pointed on his letter board and Amy sounded his words, "I prefer to be in nature."

Logan agreed, "I like to go on hikes."

"I love roller coasters," Boris answered. "It is my favorite pastime."

"No, no," Anthony replied on his letter board.

Logan asked how the others were handling math. Tom began to pace the room, restless. His mother called him back to the table but he kept pacing. He had nervous energy and he couldn't sit still. Boris began vocalizing sharply. His vocal stims were painfully loud when he felt excited so Robin handed David his sound blocking headphones. She looked around apologetically. "Sorry," she said to Boris, "but David is extremely sound sensitive." Boris's mother led him out of the room to calm down and quiet himself.

And so it went. The motley assortment of group members lurched forward, throwing ideas around. They were people who had just one social conversation a month, who communicated laboriously and slowly, so their brief messages contained an unparalleled urgency. They joked about the girl-free zone, but in truth they all desperately wished for some girl energy in the group. The females in their lives, unfortunately, were limited mostly to moms and professionals. Autism's six to one male/female ratio interfered terribly with finding an autistic girlfriend, and none had any hope of getting a non-autistic girlfriend. It was the lonely bachelor club of nonspeaking autistic guys.

They were good-looking autistic bachelors. They were all tall, with attractive faces, and Anthony was starting to look fit, though most still had their autism soft paunch and David was overly lean from food aversions. Yet physical charms aside, all had the odd behavior and mannerisms that drove romance away. They were monks, by silence and by chastity, though not by choice.

Anthony often fantasized about living Mark's life. His brother's world was rich with sports, a social life, a pretty and good-natured girlfriend. He easily lived what Anthony only dreamed of. Instead, Anthony had to find solace with his fellow silent monks, enjoying their monthly conversations with their mothers in the room, wishing he could just have normal freedom like Mark. He would be lying if he said his resentment and grief had evaporated. Still, he was grateful for his group meetings, which were light years better than where he used to be. He imagined a spectrum of loneliness, with Mark at one end, pre-communication Anthony at the other, and his current situation in the middle somewhere.

One of the mothers broke his reverie. "What should we call our group?" she asked.

Boris weighed in first, suggesting, "Typing Friends."

David said, "Typing Club."

Anthony was ready with his answer. "Autism Bachelors,"

he joked.

"Maybe we'll get a girl someday," one mother offered hopefully, but the others all laughed. Anthony's mom was gazing at him with her proud face. It brought her a lot of joy whenever he cracked a joke.

"Let's call it 'The Bachelors, for short,'" she said. And so the monkish bachelors had a new identity. Typing, nonspeaking, lonely, dateless, handsome and weird, they were a club, and their monthly meetings were an event they all looked forward to eagerly.

53

Better

Patience was not Anthony's strong suit. He wanted to be good at things immediately and if that didn't happen, he wanted to give up. Years of flubs and failure made him weary of flubbing and failing. He hated the incessant reminder that his body was disobedient. Ordinary tasks like opening pull tabs or power bars, or buttoning his shirt, or washing his hair, which should have been so easy, took exceptionally hard thought for him. That was the reason he wanted to stop trying so often. There are only so many motor failures one guy can take.

Yet, Anthony had to be honest with himself. Some things were getting easier. He noticed a kind of motor awakening. In his childhood, Anthony rarely felt his body. His mother noticed that he had a high pain threshold. He seldom cried from pain the way other kids did and even sought ways to make his body feel itself that seemed masochistic. He would walk barefoot on pebbles and pointy toys. "How can he stand that?" his mom would ask his father. Locked-in Anthony would reply in his head, *Well, at least I feel my feet now*.

But now, Anthony's body was becoming more alert. Maybe it was maturation, or maybe the exercising and communicating had opened new neural paths between his brain and his body. It felt nice being aware of his body in space. *How easy the neurotypicals have it, he thought*. They never think about how their perceptual and motor systems work together so flawlessly unless they get injured or ill. Then they notice what they've taken for granted. For Anthony it was the opposite. He noticed what he was gaining, and he was grateful. But he also noticed how far he was from where he wished to be.

Anthony had gotten used to his new routine, a constant rotation of school, homework, Marina, Jeff, Ben and Amy. At home, he had the feeling of being more a family member now than merely the object of everyone's constant attention. His parents let him just be their son more than before. Over the years, Anthony had sometimes felt that the constant obsession with his therapies, especially time-consuming, all-encompassing ABA, had made his relationship with his mom and dad more treatment-oriented than parental. He knew they had put so much work into fixing him and he was grateful in many ways. On the other hand, who likes to be reminded that he's broken all the time?

Anthony had been micromanaged his whole life, which was understandable, given his behavior. But he hated it nonetheless. Sometimes he daydreamed about just being able to be alone on a hiking trail or a beach with no strangers to stare, no parent or professional to correct him, to just savor the chance to be himself. But even his fantasies usually turned against him. He thought about what would happen if he was alone and got freaked out and overwhelmed from too much sensory input. What would happen if no one was there to control his overload? Anthony wanted space so much, but he wasn't yet ready to be free.

His mother had doggedly been practicing communicating with him. It was progressing. Their opportunities to type were less tense. She kept her cool more, so he did too. He did most of his academic work at school with Jeff, so the urgency of becoming fluent communication partners with his mother wasn't as dire as she had feared before Mark went away. This reduced her anxiety and helped her to do a better job. Anthony badly wanted his communication with his mother to improve, and he was relieved that it was less burdened by emotion. He had the hope that they might even be able to do homework together one day. All in all, home and school were much, much improved.

His main complaint at home was still Gary, who mostly related to Anthony by yelling, "Anthony, get out of my closet!" "Anthony, that's my toast!" "Anthony, you spilled my hair gel all over the floor!" "Anthony, stop standing in front of the TV!" Their dynamic definitely wasn't warm. Gary had learned to shut his feelings off as much as possible, to just cope with the annoyances of Anthony as they came.

Anthony figured that once Gary was old enough to leave home, he probably wouldn't look back. His life, as much as he could make it be, would be autism free. Mark, Anthony had reason to believe, would be the opposite. He planned to study autism in college and try to help change things. Anthony didn't blame Gary. People cope with challenges individually and Gary had different coping skills than Mark. He had just enough energy to stay afloat himself. He couldn't stay afloat and carry his autistic brother too. Mark's ability to swim and to help Anthony swim too was incredibly rare.

54

Hagerty Strikes Again

One breezy Sunday in April, Anthony, now eighteen-years-old, came home from an outing with his father and Gary to find his mother and Robin together at the kitchen table. They were talking animatedly about autism, which was nothing new. They always talked about autism. They ate it for breakfast, lunch and dinner. Anthony wondered what they would have talked about if he and David had never been born. It made him feel good that they cared so passionately about their sons that they were always striving to learn more about how they could help, but it also troubled him that autism had become such a focal point in their lives. He knew why, though. He and David constantly needed supervision and had ever since they were born. Their family members' lives had been forced to orbit autism.

David was parked in front of the television watching classic Bugs Bunny cartoons. As they had years ago at the swimming pool and on just about every occasion when the topic concerned them, Anthony and David listened to their mothers' conversation. Anthony paced nearby and David's supersonic hearing picked up the main points in between Elmer Fudd's and Bugs' repartee.

It was clear the mothers were upset about something Natasha and Dr. Hagerty were doing. They were painful figures from Anthony's past, and he preferred not to invite them into his present. He was so much happier without them. Robin was worked up. She put her coffee mug down forcefully, her tiny frame alert. She announced that they had to forge a response plan and they would need to brainstorm.

"What's going on?" Anthony's father asked.

"Hagerty," Robin said.

"No, Hagerty and Natasha," his wife said.

"What are they doing?" his father asked, his voice tensing. Robin went on her phone and read out loud, "Williamton University, Department of Applied Behavior Analysis, is pleased to invite the transformative autism educator, Dr. William Hagerty, to discuss recent alarming trends in autism education and treatment. He will be joined, following his talk, in a discussion led by Dr. Natasha Olsen, Director of *Little Stepping Stones for Autistic Children*." Robin paused. "I hate that name."

"Go on," Anthony's dad prodded.

"Okay," she continued. "What's the flavor of the month in autism treatment? Recently, remarkable claims from practitioners who allege they have the seemingly magical ability to teach low functioning, non-reading and non-communicating autistics how to type and use letter boards, sometimes virtually overnight, have become increasingly widespread. To gain insight into the phenomenon, Dr. Hagerty will explore historical cases from the field of psychology. The current claims that low-functioning autistics who have never demonstrated advanced cognition can suddenly, with certain partners, produce advanced-level scholarship demand our scrutiny and debunking. Dr. Hagerty will examine these worrisome trends by using scientific inquiry and a healthy dose of skepticism."

Robin stopped reading. Silence filled the room. Finally, Anthony's father spoke. "Looks like someone's found himself a hobby," he said sarcastically.

"Yes, at the expense of our children," Robin answered.

"Hagerty I could have predicted," Anthony's mother said.

"I don't think I'll ever forgive Natasha."

"She feels threatened," her husband said.

"The language," Robin said, "is so loaded. It's like an indoctrination."

"And preaching to the choir," Anthony's mom said. David was rocking hard in his seat in front of the television.

"I want to go to it," Robin said suddenly.

"Why subject yourself to that?" Anthony's mother sounded incredulous.

"I don't know," Robin said. "I guess someone has to be there to give a different point of view."

"They'll just act like you're crazy." Anthony's mom wanted to protect her friend. She didn't have the strength for it herself.

"So, I should just let this go unchallenged?" Robin asked.

"Everything you do is a refutation of their entire point of view," Anthony's mom said emphatically. She didn't want to see Robin hurt. "David's success is a refutation. Who cares what they think? They'll just look at you as gullible and emotional."

"I don't know," Robin said. Her head was in her hands. "It gnaws at me."

"Let it go," Anthony's father said. He was getting himself a glass of water. He wasn't as worked up as they were.

"He's powerful and influential," Robin replied.

Anthony was hovering in the background, pacing, his regular eavesdropping technique. He was sick of Dr. Hagerty, of Natasha, of their groupies, of their arrogance, of their certainty and their patronizing attitudes. *How dare they claim to know what's in my mind*, he thought. *How dare they fight to keep people locked in? How dare they claim to know autism better than me?* He paced around and vocalized.

"Look, this is upsetting the boys," his mom said.

"I should think so," Robin answered.

His father called Anthony, "What are your thoughts?" Anthony kept pacing. He was too excited to come into the kitchen and when his mom approached him with the letter board, he pushed it away. His thoughts raced and spilled around his head. He was tired of being dismissed. "Hey Anthony, relax," his father said. "It's not personal. They're lazy thinkers. They can't see out of the box."

It is personal! Anthony thought. He wasn't inclined to be forgiving. He was fed up with these people. He felt he could apply the same definers to them that they had used to define so many people with autism; "rigid, unable to make transitions, seeing parts instead of the whole." Maybe some flashcards and raisins might help.

Anthony's father looked at his son and suggested they both go sit and watch cartoons with David, who was still in front of the television but jumping up and down now on the mini-trampoline near it. He coaxed Anthony to the sofa. The Bugs Bunny cartoon playing on the TV was a classic. Bugs was in a boxing match with a gigantic, muscle-packed mountain of an opponent and Bugs, true to form, triumphed on sheer wit and irreverence. His small size and position in life as a rabbit in a world of stupid hunters, silly dogs and bombastic fools never deterred him. *A bit like me*, Anthony thought. He laughed out loud. Bugs Bunny would be his role-model for today.

In the days leading up to the lecture, Anthony's parents tried not to mention Hagerty or Natasha, but his mother found that very hard. Her body language was tense. When Anthony wasn't listening, she tried to discreetly engage her husband into talking about it but he advised her—again—to let it go. So, two days before lecture time, she picked up the phone and called Robin, who couldn't let it go. They rehashed their angry duet.

"Do they think it's better to leave a person stagnating without a means to communicate rather than try these methods?" Anthony's mom was furious and she knew she was on safe ground. "Where's their scientific inquiry?"

"It's settled, in their opinions," Robin said.

Anthony was sick of hearing about Hagerty. He tried to ignore the tension. He watched his favorite programs on television, kiddie shows that were like comfort food to his nervous brain. He knew that no matter what he did or how well he typed independently, short of overcoming his symptoms and being able to enter a room alone and type to no one, they'd never believe in him. Natasha had watched him with Marina. It wasn't enough for her. She knew that Anthony wasn't motored by Marina, but she also knew that Anthony watched kiddie shows and stimmed like a weirdo. For her, people who behaved like Anthony simply did not demonstrate the presence of a higher cognitive capacity. Certainly, in all her years working with Anthony, he had never demonstrated evidence of the cognitive capacity that Anthony's current support team was now claiming.

Anthony knew that to continue thriving he had to ignore the specialists and experts who had so much clout and so little understanding. He thought about his years of supervision, listening to Natasha get it wrong week after week. It had been so frightening. He had listened to her misguided insights then, but had not been able to correct her. He thought about how confident she had always been in her opinions. She meant well, he knew, but that hadn't lessened his fear and despair. He thought about Dr. Hagerty, who told his mother that when Anthony hugged her it wasn't out of love and that to him she was little more than a stand-in for a stuffed animal.

Thank goodness, he had been liberated from them. He knew they no longer had immediate power over his life. To him, Hagerty and Natasha were painful memories. But he was lucky. To others, they were still doing damage. They exercised direct influence over their own clients, and enormous indirect influence over countless other lives.

Anthony wanted to be rid of them but the responsibility tugged at him. He thought about what he could do.

55

The Lecture

Anthony's mother decided that she couldn't bring herself to attend the lecture. Robin couldn't keep herself away. She believed somebody had to walk into the lion's den. The lecture hall at Williamton was packed. Some members of the general public had turned out, but mostly the room had filled with excited students eager to get extra credit for hearing the famous Dr. Hagerty rebut Marina and her ilk.

Wearing a gauzy dress and flat sandals, the department head of the Applied Behavioral Analysis program at Williamton, Professor Anita Grant, a Hagerty protégé, walked onto the stage. She had been at Williamton a while. Some of Anthony's old ABA therapists had even been trained by her almost twenty years ago. She spoke quickly, in breathless tones that conveyed a sense of crisis.

"Recent trends in autism treatment have become impossible to ignore. Every day I hear from concerned students and staff who tell me that families they are working with have been looking into or trying what I can only call a new facilitation craze. Multiple news articles and television reports share heartwarming stories about nonverbal, severely autistic kids who have supposedly become proficient enough at typing, virtually overnight, to enter into general education classes. Of course, in their rush to create feel-good stories, the reporters fail to mention the hand that motors the kids through all their answers."

Professor Grant paused to scan the audience with a concerned expression. "We need to ask," she went on, "who is really doing the work? A healthy amount of skepticism is necessary when reporters fail to do their due diligence. In an alarming response to these feel-good stories, many parents are now convinced that a fully-intact and integrated person lives inside their low-functioning child just waiting to come out. Each time there is a new story in the news, my alarm bells begin to ring."

She clutched the podium. "How many desperate parents are manipulated into spending barrels of money on 'practitioners,'" she raised her fingers into air quotes, "who promise to find a way that no one else ever has? How should we respond to parents' conviction that their children can think and communicate at this mature and improbable level? In response to these concerns I reached out to the renowned Dr. William Hagerty, who truly honors us today with his words of wisdom and caution. I am so thrilled to welcome Dr. Hagerty, one of the great autism educators and thinkers."

Grant went on to describe Hagerty's formidable achievements as a theoretical trailblazer and a teaching inspiration. He received loud and long applause from the students as he strolled to the front of the stage.

Dr. Hagerty began his speech by reminding his audience that, historically, others had made comparable claims of improbable individuals possessing extraordinary abilities. Perhaps the most illuminating example, he continued, one with clear parallels to the current dilemma, was the rather famous case of the miraculous Hans, or Clever Hans, as he was commonly known. Those in the audience unfamiliar with Hans soon learned that he was not a human being. No, Dr. Hagerty chose to make a parallel between nonspeaking autistic humans—members of a species that possessed the potential for innate language ability and high cognition—and an intelligent horse.

"Hans was a truly remarkable horse," Dr. Hagerty said, strolling as he talked with a clip-on microphone stuck to his lapel. He was even heavier now, with a thinning head of white hair that seemed to accentuate his narrow nose.

Hagerty flashed an old picture of a large horse onto the screen. "Hans had successfully convinced huge audiences in turn-of-the-century Germany that he understood human speech and could calculate fractions, square roots, and other math equations." The audience tittered. It was a comical concept. "He communicated by tapping his front hoof to questions presented to him in spoken and in written German. Imagine seeing a horse that could read and calculate."

Hagerty stopped for effect. "It was incredible and people searched for answers. Were horses particularly able and brilliant and we humans had not been aware of this mathematical, literary and intellectual ability for thousands of years? Was Hans simply a uniquely brilliant individual horse, still indicating an intelligence in the equine previously unknown to humankind? Or was this an elaborate and highly convincing fraud? I ask you, what do you think was going on with Hans?" He surveyed his audience. Some hands went up.

"Yes?" Dr. Hagerty said pointing to a young woman in the front row.

"Hans was trained by his handler," she yelled out.

"That's a reasonable conclusion," he replied, in professor mode. "However, I'm going to throw in a monkey wrench. His handler took no payment for their performances. He was not trying to profit from gullible audiences. He genuinely believed in Hans' ability."

Another student volunteered, "Maybe the trainer was unaware that he was somehow providing Hans cues."

"So perhaps it was subconscious cuing," Dr. Hagerty said.

After a few moments of discussion on this theme, he asked, "Why has no one suggested the possibility that Hans actually did math calculations or read?"

"He was a horse," one young man offered from the third row. "He had no ability to think at that level." The crowd continued to call out similar answers about a horse's limited cognitive ability to do mathematics.

After a few moments, Dr. Hagerty said, "I'd like to show you a film clip." Dr. Hagerty went to his computer and began to play a film clip of a deeply autistic young man bopping to his own internal stim music. He bent up and down at the waist, flicking his wrists in butterfly twists and yelling grunts and groans. "Here is a severely autistic young man named Harry," Dr. Hagerty observed. "How aware do you think Harry is of his surroundings?"

"He is unaware," a student offered.

"He is in a world of his own," another said.

Dr. Hagerty resumed playing the video as his audience stared, engrossed. In it, the boy's mother says to him, "Go get your book." He continued to flick and dance. She says to the camera, "Harry doesn't understand what I'm asking." She says to her son again, "Harry, go get your book." He looks up briefly, then continues to flick and dance some more in his herky-jerky choreography. "Get book," she repeats several more times, simplifying her language. She finally retrieves the toddler book and gives it to her son. Harry drops it on the floor.

When the video clip ended, Hagerty waited, letting the audience murmurs die down, building expectation.

"How would you react if I told you this boy is now in college and graduated high school with honors?"

Now the audience fell silent.

"It's not possible," a student finally called out.

"He would have had to be facilitated by another person who did the work for him."

Again Dr. Hagerty looked around at his audience. They were a bright bunch. "Do you notice a corollary between this young man and the story of the brilliant Hans?" The students responded energetically. It was so obvious to them that neither the clever horse nor the low-functioning boy understood at the levels that were claimed.

"I think there is one big difference," a voice in the audience raised.

"Yes?" Dr. Hagerty responded.

"The horse is an animal and the autistic boy is a human being."

"Very true," Dr. Hagerty said. "How does that make a difference here?"

"Humans have the capacity to read and write and communicate in language. Horses don't."

"Absolutely," Dr. Hagerty said, sliding his glasses up his nose. "But we are not comparing humans in general to horses. We are comparing *Harry* to a horse. A brilliant horse and a low-functioning human. Why should I assume Harry here has the capacity to understand? His mother, who knows him best, doesn't think he does. He was unable to follow the simple instruction, 'Get book.' He didn't know what to do with the book. He dropped it on the floor. His relationship with the world is significantly less engaged than was Hans'. Hans paid attention. Harry has not yet acquired the ability to attend to a world beyond his own internal compulsions."

One student asked, "Do you believe Harry has no understanding of language?"

"Let us not say 'none.' Let us assume it is severely limited to about fifty or so words. Would a person who can read, write and perform academically behave like this? Our external behavior reflects our interior world; in Harry's case, an interior panorama of utter chaos. I believe that whether intentional, or by missionary zeal and self-delusion, the so-called teachers of typing to boys like Harry have made grandiose claims of abilities never seen before. As were made about Hans." Heads nodded throughout the audience. "When I mentioned earlier that Harry had graduated high school with honors and was enrolled in college, I heard people gasp," Hagerty prodded. "Why is that?"

A hand rose, "Because he is clearly not engaged with the world and is unable to respond to a two-word instruction. I think sending a person like that to college is child abuse. It's something the parents do for themselves."

"My dog wants to go to college," someone catcalled. Everyone laughed.

Dr. Grant, who was sitting on a stool at the side of the stage, replied, "Shall I get him an application?" Students snickered and a few even clapped their hands appreciatively.

Dr. Hagerty brought the room back under control. "How can we look at these claims scientifically? I am a man of science and must demand evidence, methodology that can be tested and replicated before I simply accept claims that a young man like Harry, always assisted, is now a scholar. You may be dealing with desperate parents who cannot accept their children's limitations. Saviors appear, promising, not recovery because that can't be faked, but the magical discovery of untapped linguistic abilities. I say, prove it. I don't need to observe these practitioners or meet these children. I need data. I need studies. I don't need to talk to an emotional mother telling me what her kid can do. I need Harry to do a double-blind test, with random testers, to type alone in a room. Get the aide away. Kick out Mom. Then I'll tell you if the claims are true."

Dr. Hagerty paced the stage. "Theory of mind. Perhaps Hans had it. Does Harry?"

"Can you elaborate on what happened to Hans, and to Harry?" a student asked.

"Hans, that marvelous animal, was indeed a precocious and clever horse. But he was not literate nor could he solve math equations," Dr. Hagerty answered. "He did, however, have great sensitivity and he responded to minute cues from his handler, which, as I mentioned earlier, were totally subconsciously given. Hans tapped his foot until the handler's movement slightly shifted. Then he stopped. This always coincided with the correct answer. He was debunked by a man of science, psychologist Oskar Pfungst. But there is no question, Hans was a phenomenal reader of people and of subtle body cues. Now we must ask, is Harry equally perceptive? Is *his* trainer equally unaware of her cues? I theorize that Harry, based on his lack of awareness and lack of responsiveness to his mother, lacks a theory of mind equal to Hans'. But perhaps his college career will prove otherwise."

He paused for a moment and then said with a smile, "Actually, I have no idea what Harry is doing. I have never met him nor do I know anything about him or his education, beyond what this short clip, which I chanced upon on the Internet, reveals. But looking at Hans and Harry side by side reminds us of the gap between claims and reality. No reasonable scientist would believe that a Harry has an inner genius that only one person can unlock. Harry cannot get a book or listen to his mother. His behavior is disengaged and self-stimulatory, yet we are told, and asked to believe, that he, or children just like him, can suddenly do algebra or write insightful essays. The skill is invariably displayed only with one facilitator; it cannot be generalized. The child cannot replicate it with everyone, as occurs in genuine communication. This reveals that it is *training* that creates the result. Intended or not, it is Clever Harry…oops, Clever Hans, all over again." He chuckled at his slip of the tongue.

Dr. Hagerty concluded his talk. His appreciative audience stood and applauded. "I can stay and answer a few questions," he offered. "Then I'll let the able Natasha Olsen continue the discussion."

"Why do you think it isn't necessary to observe the typing directly?" one student asked. "Wouldn't that be inquiring scientifically?"

"No, not at all," Dr. Hagerty replied. "They have to have data first. Then I'll take the time to observe if the data passes the smell test."

He moved to the next question. It was about Marina's daughter, who typed alone at a keyboard and had been studied by a respected team of researchers who had found her communication to be genuinely hers. "How do you account for her success?"

"She is one in a million, no question," Hagerty conceded. "There may be different reasons for this. Perhaps she isn't an autist but has another disability that looks like autism. Maybe she has savant language skills. We cannot say why, but clearly, she is unique. We cannot generalize because of the skills of one individual. Some people simply have unique abilities."

Dr. Hagerty took a few more questions, then he announced that there would be a short break of fifteen minutes after which Natasha Olsen, director of the behavioral agency *Little Stepping Stones for Autistic Children*, would be available to continue the discussion. He was getting older and these lectures fatigued him. Handing off the baton had become his pattern when he lectured and it worked well for him.

After the break, Dr. Grant went to the podium again and described how valuable it was, after Dr. Hagerty's illuminating lecture, for students to hear the perspective of someone on the frontlines, someone who dealt with these claims in her personal practice. "I'm delighted to welcome Natasha Olsen," she said, beaming, "who brings with her a wealth and depth of experience."

Elegant and stylish in designer clothes and high heels, Natasha stepped to the podium. She made an impressive figure. She spoke briefly about the many trends in autism treatment she had seen come and go over the years. This one, she said, was most alarming because it seemed to indicate a great deal of denial on the part of parents. Natasha shared an anecdote about a highly autistic teenaged boy she knew whose family had come to believe he communicated fluently and independently after meeting with Marina. Natasha described how she had been able to observe him in a session and she noticed that Marina talked non-stop, held the letter board for him and sometimes even touched his shoulder. To ascertain if his apparent abilities were dependent on these prompts, she asked her own highly competent staff person, his case supervisor, to independently assess and verify his skill level. But the supervisor got no response from him whatsoever. Moreover, Natasha went on, that very same day, the boy's teacher claimed that this same young man had communicated directly with her (though, of course, Natasha's staff person was not present to observe it). Not only had the boy allegedly communicated, Natasha continued, according to the teacher, that previously unresponsive boy had used his letter board to hurl the f-bomb at Natasha's staffer the moment her back was turned. She paused to allow time for titters and gasps.

"Seriously," Natasha said, nodding at the audience. "These

are the kinds of delicate and highly emotional situations we now have to be ready to deal with."

Robin was seated in the sixth row, off to the side. She gaped. Her eyes grew big. She recognized the story she was hearing immediately. She had heard it from Anthony's mother's perspective.

"Do you think it's possible he communicated with one person and not the other?" a voice asked.

"He knew my staff person for years in a relationship of trust," Natasha replied. "She has lots of experience with autistic kiddos. Why would he not be able to replicate the skill with her? Clearly, to demonstrate a real skill, the child must be able to replicate that skill in all settings and with all people."

Robin was shaking her head, simultaneously angry and glad she had been there to hear this.

"Could anxiety be a contributing factor?" a student asked.

"Anxiety should not shut down the entire communication mechanism," Natasha answered. "Moreover, he had no reason to be anxious with this staff person, who always approached him warmly and had great concern for his wellbeing."

"I recognize that there are some situations in which a person's communication appears to be questionable but I think there are other people whose pointing and typing looks convincing," a student commented from the middle of the auditorium. "Shouldn't we observe those cases on an individual basis, just like neuro-researchers did with Marina Folvino's daughter, Jane?"

"When they type like Jane Folvino, of course," Natasha conceded. "I would like MRI testing as well, to indicate if she has another brain anomaly, but the claims we are focusing on are those made regarding people who have nowhere near the independence or skills of a Jane Folvino. We really are looking at apples and oranges."

An angry voice called out, "Jane didn't have her degree of independence either when she was just starting out. It is a process. You understand that, right?" It was Robin.

"Progression is important," Natasha answered, unflappable, poised, "but so is validity. It is important that with great claims comes proof, and these kids lack provability."

"Maybe at first," Robin said, "but they progress and become more and more independent. You have to take that into account. I'm speaking to you as one of those so-called emotional mothers. My son learned to type from Marina Folvino and he is now in general education." The audience murmured and then grew quiet as Robin continued. "His behavior is better. He is happier. He follows instructions better. You can't boil this down to your tests. The brain is too complex for simple answers. What about the human element? Dr. Hagerty and you talk *about* nonverbal people. You speak *for* them." Robin was nervous and it came through in her quick sentences. It was as though she felt she only had a flash in time to convey her message.

"I see you feel quite passionately about this. It is an emotional issue," Natasha remarked. "This is why evidence-based data is so crucial. Anecdotes are compelling but can be deceptive. Thank you so much for sharing your feelings with us," she said to Robin. She then turned to another person in the audience, effectively cutting Robin off.

"Do you think this treatment trend will eventually run its course?" the student asked. Natasha tilted her head, then fired off a ready answer.

"It will probably follow the arc of other popular, invalidated treatments that had their heyday. Certainly, this is something we need to monitor."

Robin, who had sat silently throughout Dr. Hagerty's talk and most of Natasha's, was furious. All her emotions had risen to the surface. She *was* an emotional mother. She stood up, all five feet two of her, and marched dramatically out of the room. At the doorway she shouted, "They cannot speak! They cannot fight back!"

There were uncomfortable murmurs throughout the audience. A moment later, Natasha resumed her questions and answers. Robin had certainly demonstrated the emotional side of the debate.

56

The Response

The next day, Anthony eavesdropped as his mother spoke with Robin on the phone about the lecture, gleaning what happened from her responses. His mother noticed him and asked Robin if she could put the call on speaker-phone so Anthony could hear. As Anthony paced back and forth, Robin recounted the key points in detail.

There really was nothing surprising in what they said. Yet he couldn't help but feel angry. Natasha and Hagerty had worked with him personally for so many years. That was true. They were betrayers. Natasha was a betrayer. No, that wasn't it. Anthony reminded himself that they had always underestimated and misunderstood. Theoretically they were totally consistent. They weren't likely to alter their viewpoint now after they had devoted their entire careers to it.

The next day, Anthony met with Marina during his usual appointment. She prepared to work with him on his tablet typing, using word predictions.

"What would you like to talk about?" she asked.

"I want to write a letter," he typed.

"Okay, to who?" Marina asked. She was always game. Always respectful.

"Dr. Hagerty," he answered.

"Okay," she said. "Can I film you?"

"Yes, go," he typed.

Anthony was ready. He immediately began to type his letter.

"Dear Dr. Hagerty, I am not a horse. It maybe is a surprise for you, but I never was one either."

Marina laughed. "Go on," she said.

He typed slowly. It took him almost fifteen minutes. "I have messed up neurology, but it is still human neurology. I process language like a human. This is a surprise to you, I know. Horses are not wired to understand complex language, humans are. Even nonspeaking humans."

"Letter board," Anthony typed. He was tired from the intense concentration the iPad took for him and he wanted to point on his letter board, which was faster with its bigger letters than his tablet. Marina switched out Anthony's tablet for a letter board and held it steady. Today was about Anthony expressing himself, not about improving his tablet skill. He went on, with Marina reading the words he pointed to out loud, then jotting them down so his letter could be transcribed when finished.

"I understand everything. I always have," Anthony continued. "My problem is output. My brain doesn't communicate well with my motor system. I may look like I don't understand but don't let that fool you. I do understand. When I was small and couldn't communicate, I was totally locked in my body. I couldn't correct my experts. Now I can," he added, "and you should listen."

"No more. I'm tired," he typed. That was for Marina.

"Great letter," she said. "To be continued?" she asked.

"Yes," Anthony said. It was long overdue and he felt a sense of relief. "My turn to speak," he told her.

In the car on the way home he thought about his letter and what he wanted it to say. The next session and the one after that started the same way. His mom sat in the back of the room. Marina set up her camera. She brought out the old letter. Anthony composed. Today he offered up an insider's look at his neurology.

"I have a neurological condition that has impacted my life

since birth," he pointed on his letter board. "My intellect functions pretty well, though I do take in a surplus of information. This is tough because my sensory system can get overwhelmed by bombardments of auditory, visual and tactile input. The worst feature is the extreme apraxia I face. It is total body apraxia. Mouth, tongue, hands, everything. My brain tries to talk to my body but my body has trouble receiving the message. It sometimes gets it. Often it doesn't, or my body gets locked in patterns of motor memory. These are neurological loops and stims. Or my body may disobey me altogether and move as it alone wishes. One awful feature is that many people assume I can't understand language. They misconstrue apraxic, impulsive bodies for low intellectual abilities." Anthony took a break. He was getting close to the finale. He wanted the psychiatrist to feel what he felt, to finally understand.

"Can you imagine, Dr. Hagerty, being locked in your body like this?" he continued. "Not only is the prison horrid but specialists treat you like you're stupid and simple because you look stupid and simple to them. It is easy to understand why. Most specialists I saw lacked imagination in seeing my potential and in recognizing the true origin of my behavior. Some have even become famous for their incorrect conclusions."

After three sessions Anthony had finished. "Very powerful," Marina concluded. Anthony was thinking about how Dr. Hagerty would never believe that he had written his letter. He remembered the imaginary letter he had written to him during his silent years. *Dear Dr. Hagerty, Shut up, shut up, shut up*. That was still a good letter.

"Do you want to add anything?" Marina asked.

"I am not a horse," he typed.

"Is that it?"

"Yes," he typed.

"Do you want to send it?"

"Not sure," he typed.

"Why not?"

"He will think I'm Hans and you wrote it."

"For sure, but don't let that silence you," Marina said. "The question is whether it's more worthwhile to work with others who are more open-minded or to put so much energy and feeling into an immovable object."

Anthony thought this made sense. He was letting Hagerty and Natasha poison him, even though they no longer really mattered. They were out of his life. They weren't likely to change. Maybe he just needed to write his letter, not send his letter. He again imagined Hagerty opening the email. "Oh, I remember Anthony," he'd say. "A boy with no theory of mind, no language usage, no attention span, no relatedness. This letter proves my points perfectly. He did not write it."

Anthony flapped a little. "No, I'll send it to them," he typed. "I'm tired of being silent and I'm tired of being silenced."

"Okay," his mom said quietly. "To Dr. Hagerty and Natasha. Anyone else?"

"Anita Grant, department head," Anthony typed," "and the student newspaper."

"Oh, wow," his mom said. "You sure?"

"I'm sure I'm not a horse," he pointed. "I'm sure I understand language and I'm sick of being told what I am by experts. I'm the expert."

Anthony knew he wouldn't change their minds but he was glad he had the chance to defend himself. Maybe he'd have a positive impact on some of the students who had been in the audience. Maybe he'd be attacked. He decided he was okay, whatever the outcome. He was tired of not being able to respond. He had spent an entire life not responding to incorrect statements about him during Natasha supervisions, various therapies and Hagerty consultations. He would no longer accept being silenced by his body.

Anthony decided that he wasn't really interested in how they would react at the university or in their offices. He simply needed not to be passive, not to feel as he had when Cindy had grabbed him so harshly by the face during their speech therapy session and he was powerless to do or say anything about it. This time, he had his voice. It was his silent voice, his pointing voice, but it was his own.

For once, no matter what happened, Hagerty, Natasha and Professor Opinionated had not gotten the last word. He had the ability to respond. He felt liberated, excited even.

57

Ready

The next day, Anthony was back in school. He had a good feeling inside. He had to acknowledge the positive things in his life. He was now out of Miss Harris' class for three subjects and he was integrated and performing at a level he never imagined he would get to in school. He didn't mind Miss Harris' room as much as before because he knew she was totally on his side and that made him happy. He also knew that, little by little, he would move into general education because he was succeeding, in spite of all the warnings and concerns of Bette and Mrs. Norris. It was new for Anthony to feel so much satisfaction in his life. He had never wanted for love or pleasurable activities, like swimming or stimming, but his life had been deprived of meaning. He had lacked attainable goals, purposeful education, friendship and of course, communication. Now, things were looking up.

Anthony had no illusions of recovery. His autism was there to stay until he died. This meant he had to learn to embrace life *with* it and find ways to reduce his resentment and frustration. He once imagined that communication would make him more normal, but he now realized that autism clung to him like a vine. He could express his thoughts now and even respond to his know-it-all experts, but he remained just as autistic as he had been at five years old. He had seen some symptoms recede and other challenges emerge, but Anthony now knew that if he were to succeed it would have to be with all his symptoms present for all the world to see. He would have to succeed as a noticeable weirdo.

It helped him to see how much happier his family was, as if a dark cloud of despair and fatigue was starting to lift from his household. The future made him no promises, but that is true for anyone. What Anthony had now was a taste of more. He walked into his history class, jumping, smiling, his aide walking behind him. Anthony felt ready to take on the lesson and ready to learn. He was not lost inside and Autismland held no lure in that moment. He was the most unusual student in the room and he had learned to live with that. He was ready.

Printed in Great Britain
by Amazon